CONTENTS

Float Line Glassmakers of 1957.

THE GLOBAL MIRACLE OF FLOAT GLASS

A tribute to St Helens and
its glass workers

by TOM GRUNDY

Front Cover Illustration:
The lighting by Lord Harry of the
First New Float Tank, C.H. 3, in 1962 at
Cowley Hill Works, in the company of Sir Alastair Pilkington,
the originator of the Float Glass process.

FOREWORD

Tommy Grundy has written the story of Float Glass right from the early development struggles, through to the first success and then to the spread of Float throughout the world as the universal process for making Flat Glass.

What is very unusual is that he has written the story from the point of view of the people who actually made the glass. They took the molten glass and converted it in the float bath into a flat ribbon. This may sound simple and easy, but it was a tremendous struggle and the glassmakers who worked on the process did an heroic job. They were so dedicated to their job that the problem was to try to avoid them doing too much. Without their efforts Float would never have come through to success.

Tommy Grundy himself took a leading part during many years both during the development period and during the time when we were teaching the world how to make Float Glass. This book is a tribute from Tommy Grundy to all the Glassmakers in Pilkingtons who made float and gave so generously of their time and effort to make it the success it has become.

I would like to pay a tribute to Tommy Grundy himself, who set the highest standard of leadership and commitment and who encouraged and inspired the men who worked with him.

Sir Alastair Pilkington, F.R.S.

INTRODUCTION

THIS BOOK is to highlight the essential contribution by shopfloor production workers to the success of the Pilkington float glass process.

All too often we read or hear of industrial successes when tribute is paid to the Research and Development efforts, financial undertakings, the invention itself or the inventor, but very little is published about the shopfloor worker — the effect on his working conditions, changes in his environment, and many other changes which can even affect his home life — which ultimately the speed of the success of the invention relied upon and as did actually happen with float glass.

To write this book honestly and effectively I have to make many references to myself because I was a shopfloor worker at the beginning of the development stages of the float process. I do not have any type of schooling qualifications, whether it be 'O' Level, 'A' Level or anything else, for the only qualifications I have had have been hard work, loyalty, commonsense and the enjoyment of working with people, similar to the rest of the team. To be honest and fair to others connected with the development of float glass I must make it clear that I am concentrating on the float line glass Manual Production Furnace men who had to accept and adapt themselves to the new environment in glassmaking right from the development stage.

After the initial production success the same shopfloor workers had to adapt themselves to the training of workers for future expansion. When Pilkington licensed the float process, the same shopfloor workers had the task of training their opposite numbers in the licensee teams. Later the same men went out to other countries to work, supervise and make float glass.

It was another case of the workmen having to adapt themselves to new foreign environmental problems owing to climate, methods and language problems.

Actually they were the true ambassadors of float glass in a big new world. During the changeover years from plate glass to float glass, many sacrifices were made by these men and their families which ultimately changed the Pilkington flat glass works. The town of St Helens itself had to readjust in many ways to handle the reorganisation of the glass industry brought about by float.

Horse drawn transport.

2

1

BRIEF HISTORY OF THE COMPANY

PILKINGTON p.l.c. originated in 1826 in the St Helens Crown Glass Company, founded with the technical knowledge and ability of John William Bell and capital from three of the most influential local families, the Bromilows, the Greenalls and the Pilkingtons. William Pilkington was one of the original shareholders, and he was later joined by his elder brother Richard. It was renamed Greenall & Pilkington in 1829 and, after the withdrawal of Peter Greenall, the firm was retitled Pilkington Brothers in 1849.

At this time, the window glass industry was almost exclusively concerned with producing crown glass. This type of manufacture was gradually superseded in the late 1830's by the introduction of sheet glass made by the blown cylinder process.

Pilkington introduced tank furnaces for the manufacture of sheet glass, and also decided to manufacture plate glass, choosing as its site Cowley Hill, on the outskirts of St Helens.

Cowley Hill glass works has been at the forefront of technical advancement in the glass industry since Pilkington Brothers built the factory in 1873.

The Company decided to begin the manufacture of plate glass in that year — 100 years after it was first made — and work began on a factory to do so at Cowley Hill near Gerards Bridge.

The Cowley Hill factory had the largest casting hall in the world, with three 30-pot furnaces and 60 annealing kilns. The

*Sheet operator controlling
Forming and Drawing.*

4

first plate was cast at Cowley Hill in July 1876.

Plate glass was the luxury product of the glass industry and it was made by the casting method. The molten glass was poured onto an iron table and rolled like a piece of pastry into a large flat plate. This was pushed into an annealing kiln where it stayed for 10 days while the glass cooled very gradually. The plate was then ground and polished to remove the rough, dull surface produced by contact with the roller and table. This process reduced by half the thickness of the cast glass but the end product was flat, parallel and highly polished.

Large plate windows and mirrors became very fashionable in Britain in the late 19th century and production soon increased at Cowley Hill. Over the years money was ploughed back into the plate glass factory to keep it right up to date. When electricity was introduced in the 1890's, Pilkingtons became one of the first firms to use it.

In the 1920's a continuous method of producing plate glass from a tank, rather than pots, was developed and Cowley Hill was the first works to use the new process. The continuous grinding and polishing process was also first introduced at Cowley Hill. These developments significantly improved the efficiency of the plate glass manufacturing process.

In the 1930's yet another Pilkington invention was installed first at Cowley Hill when the twin grinder and polisher was introduced. This revolutionary idea meant both sides of the ribbon of glass could be polished at the same time.

In the late 1950's Cowley Hill was the location for the final development work on the most revolutionary invention in glass making history, the **FLOAT PROCESS**.

Sheet glass is drawn vertically up a tower of about 30 feet in height. When it emerges at the top, often being guided by rollers and being gradually cooled, it is cut in large plates and transferred to the warehouse.

Annealing Lehr.

2

EARLY DAYS

Let us take a look at Cowley Hill Works around 1948 before the float glass invention when 3,800 were being employed. The starting and finishing times for workers were hailed by a large siren which could be heard for as much as 3 or 4 miles away from work. It was steam controlled and would always blow three minutes before starting time, and then on starting, but on starting time it would blow a second or two longer and also a little louder. This happened at finishing time as well, three minutes before finishing time and on finishing time. As a matter of fact all St Helens could set their clocks on the sound of the buzzer.

The first three minute sound was to warn the workers that they had only three minutes to clock on otherwise they would be late for work, and after that, one minute only was allowed after the final buzzer. If they were late after that, pay was deducted accordingly.

When finishing work the buzzer blew three minutes before finishing time. That was the signal to stop work and wash your hands ready for the final finishing buzzer. As a matter of fact practically every housewife or mother would say, there is the three minute buzzer and I'll have to put the kettle on, or go to the chip shop, or put the pies in the oven, Jack will be in for his meal in so many minutes.

Yes, the Pilkington buzzers set the working and dining times for most of St Helens.

Next we look inside the factory, and because contract labour was not employed those days, there were buildings for every type of maintenance trades workers, each trade having their own departmental buildings, electricians, joiners, plumbers, fitters, brickies, and so on. Also at Cowley Hill there was a six storey building which was situated at the very highest point in the factory which also happened to be the highest point in St Helens town. This was known as the pot rooms, where all the clay work for the pot furnaces and plate glass furnaces was moulded and baked, and could be seen from miles away.

There was an internal railway system which was connected up to the main outside railway system, this railway system would service every department. We used railways for all glassmaking materials, and glass delivery to customers. Those days we made our own gas and this meant that all the coal was transported by railway into the factory. We also had our own power station which made steam and electricity from coal, which came in by the same railway system.

Yes, we had four large coal gas producers, three large chimneys from the furnaces, and one large chimney from the power station. The chimneys could be seen pouring the smoke out for miles around.

Because of grinding and polishing we needed approximately four times more land space to house the grinding and polishing machines than was needed for the furnace and annealing lehrs of glassmaking, and the whole factory seemed to be squeezed into a small stuffy area.

I think the reason for this was the space taken by grinding and polishing. All the waste from the glass and materials used, especially from grinding, had to be deposited on land space outside the factory. This waste was known as burgy.

Burgy was slurried away along wooden chutes and over a period of time it had accumulated to the effect that there was hundreds of acres of waste sand etc., known as burgy banks, and of course Pilkington had to keep acquiring land which was very expensive. There was no use for this burgy by anyone so it was a matter of conserving as much land as possible for this purpose.

The sand used in glassmaking was field sand and had to be washed and sifted before usage. For this purpose we had a huge area where the sand was washed known as the sandwash which was a noticeable building on the country side of the factory.

8

The mixing room was a small building where the glassmaking materials were mixed and transported to the furnaces in skips drawn by tractors. The broken glass known as cullet was pick and shovelled and transported with a similar skip and tractor.

There were no car parks, there were just bicycle sheds and motor cycle parks and also every emergency service building like fire, surgery etc. was on site.

As the float glass invention was being advanced up to today's level, there were big changes taking place over the period of years, and if we look at Cowley Hill Works today, we are making more glass in Cowley Hill but missing is:

(a)   The works buzzer and the thousands of people rushing out of the factory on time.
(b)   The internal railway system has finished and all transportation is by road vehicles.
(c)   There are no dirty coal gas producers as now oil or natural gas is used.
(d)   No buildings with grinding and polishing machines, in place there are now stock rooms etc.
(e)   No tall buildings known as the pot rooms, these have been demolished.
(f)   Because of outside contracting many trades buildings have been reorganised or demolished.
(g)   No waste slurry chutes leading from the grinders to the burgy banks.
(h)   No sand washing area.
(i)   Most noticeable shortage of work people.

What do we see today?

(a)   Large enclosed car parks set in garden surrounds inside and outside of the factory.
(b)   Where the old maintenance buildings have been demolished there are flower beds and lawns creating a better environment.
(c)   A new up-to-date self service canteen, nearer to work places, and modern wash rooms etc.
(d)   All workers issued with the Pilkington overalls and new types of safety clothing.
(e)   Road transport only being used, and clean and better road surfaces.

9

(f) A new tall modern mixing room which is also a factory land mark supplying both furnaces with glass making materials by the conveyor system.

(g) Where there used to be a big rubbish tip and burgy banks inside the works boundary there is now a big new float line and warehousing sections which can be identified by its tall chimney and colour scheme, mostly blue roofing.

(h) All the burgy banks inside and outside the factory boundary have now been beautified by the planting of trees and shrubs to give a huge forest or garden appearance instead of the dull waste sand appearance.

(i) There is now a spacious new entrance for all transport in and out of the factory directly to the main road surrounded by grass verge, lawns and trees.

(j) Because of the float lines there is also a new factory in Washway Lane built by British Oxygen Company to supply gases to all the St Helens float glass lines.

The times have changed and the majority of workers come to work all nice and smart in their cars, and there is nothing to stop them from going home after work in the same clean smart condition because every facility is available inside the factory for them to do this under present working conditions.

Pilkington started glassmaking in St. Helens in 1826 which means glassmaking today could be classed as an inherited skill, but to understand this book more clearly it is most important that a specific breakdown of departments should be known to the reader.

It is important to recognise the responsibilities, the gradings, and functions operating in the manufacture of, and during the changeover period of plate glass to float glass. I will split it up into:

(a) Administration, which covers white collar workers.

(b) Maintenance departments, covered by apprenticeships of all trades.

(c) Glass cutters, who were tradesmen.

(d) Workers who were on the unskilled labour market for any job e.g. furnacemen, glassmakers.

(e) Research and Development was in its infancy, with plate glass experiments being heavily backed up by furnacemen.

Broadly speaking, the administration, maintenance, cutters and warehousing and Research and Development departments are very important essentials but free to move around flexible away from the hot temperature conditions of glassmaking, and it was the monotony of this environment which I feel was a major factor in glass manufacture.

The furnace men were the glassmakers and they had a unique position only known to the glass industry, for this rate of knowledge and progress came from hard work, loyalty and dedication to the job, knowing that if anything happened their experience and hard earned knowledge could not be bargained for elsewhere, only on furnace work which kept them at a job disadvantage elsewhere.

The rate of progress through the furnace glassmaking dept. was brushing up, spading broken glass, feeding materials into the hot furnace, controlling temperature conditions and also being available for all types of emergencies with the hot glass and furnace accidents which needed glass melting knowledge and responsibility.

Next was the glass forming knowledge, the know-how of forming conditions for width, thickness, speed, quality, and machine responsibility. These hot conditions came under furnace work. After the forming machines came the annealing of the glass knowledge, e.g. the flatness, the correct stress and strain measurements for cutting and handling conditions. These came under the furnaceman's control and responsibility.

All this sums up the fact that glassmaking from the raw cold material to actual cold saleable glass was virtually controlled by 'non-skilled workers'.

The rate of promotion was through the spade to operator, chargehand, foreman, and day senior foreman, and many a time good glass depended on the furnace people working as a team which only they knew how.

Because of the abnormal conditions, people were reluctant to come into glassmaking which meant the labour turnover was erratic.

The workers who did stay with furnace work proved themselves to be in most cases, good loyal family people.

It was because of family loyalty that most were prepared to accept the hard conditions of glassmaking to keep themselves in employment, and those days with the hot heavy hard work, and many-a-time having to work long hours overtime, I am sure family love and unity made a massive contribution to the success of glassmaking.

In the years 1946-1953 approximately, the men coming into glassmaking were men around 25-40 years of age, and were just beginning to settle down with their wives, children and families after war service, establishing their homes and lives, which proved to be a great asset to Pilkingtons.

Of course, Pilkington's were being appreciated by the work people, because with the firm being owned by a good Christian family, it was their policy to create as much employment as possible and in many jobs they employed more people than they actually needed at the time.

I, like some of the other men, came home from the Armed Forces to a wife and two children so that my first ambition was to have a home of my own.

To keep up the payments on the mortgage and furnishings I had to work hard, for furnace work was the lowest paid job which meant all overtime pay was welcome, which also applied to many of the team. Also it was noticeable that the workmen began to mould themselves into good working and social teams.

It was often said those days that all a person needed to work in the tank furnaces, was brute force and ignorance which was one of the reasons for a big turnover of labour, and because of this, I was able to move along the line very quickly.

Having no education certificates of any description, I had no sights of promotion in my mind.

It was August 1947 when my first important glassmaking challenge came along. I was working morning shift and I had just got home at 2.00pm when I was called into work. The glassmaking manager, who was a man who had worked his way up through the working ranks, asked me to take charge of No. 1 glassmaking line.

This was the beginning of my glassmaking challenge, but fortunately I had a great team of workmen on my shift, who gave me every type of encouragement needed for a new foreman on his first assignment.

In those days a shift foreman had full responsibility for men, materials, plant and good glassmaking. There were many times between 5.30pm and 8.00am the following morning, holiday times and weekends, when we had no contact with senior management, unless we sent a man on a bicycle to the manager's home. It was then I realised every section of the job meant sweat and hard work, even burns, scalds, gas explosions, fatigue, glass cuts etc. It was very important to keep the hard working teams

ıl men, loyal and conscientious and happy at their work, even
ı the extent of socialising by having a beer with them after
.\ork.

The senior management noticed and realised that some of the
ıcn had good potentials. I was one who was earmarked as a
ı:actical man for the future of glass development work.

At our Cowley Hill Factory we had a manager who was very
-en to improve his glassmaking and formed his own develop-
ıent section.

I was one of the team to assist on the practical side of the
 evelopment work on glass melting.

This type of work meant that I was learning more about
ınatters such as melting temperatures, refractories, refining,
uels, annealing. Also I had the opportunity to travel to our other
ıactories and furnaces, and to experiment and demonstrate new
ıechniques we were developing for better and more economical
.vays of glassmaking.

It was during this time in my working life in 1948 I first met
Alastair Pilkington, now Sir Alastair Pilkington, three years
before float was invented. We met and did a little work on one
of our furnaces, but it was when I was asked to go to Doncaster
with him to do some furnace development work that I began to
understand him, for we had never really had a conversation
about anything apart from casual remarks about glassmaking.

I met Sir Alastair at Manchester station on the Monday
morning and during this train journey to Doncaster we had a
good chat about our wartime experiences including his return
to Cambridge to finish his studies, and I told him about my
return from the forces to be a glass worker doing my best to get
a home together for my wife and two children.

There was just Alastair and myself working together. For one
week we stayed in different hotels. He stayed in the Reindeer
Hotel in Doncaster and I stayed in the Danum Hotel. We never
met socially out of work.

At work I was responsible for the practical side of the
experiment which involved the preparation of hot refractories,
and the remaining hot practical work that was required. Sir
Alastair did the academical side, working out the results of the
experiments.

We both knew that we were working for the same target
which was to improve the glass quality. Also this was the
beginning of a working relationship, which at this time, was

13

something unforeseen.

In 1950 due to a trade recession one of the plate glass furnaces closed down which meant that nearly half of the men had to go on other jobs around the factory, e.g. labouring for anyone where there was a need, and some 20% left the firm altogether.

It was about 1953 when the management realised that if Pilkington were going to go into the development of float glass making methods, more men would be needed in the furnaces, so that the experienced glassmakers could be released to assist in the new development programme.

Pilkington Development Department had been doing a lot of experimental work and at that time, Sir Alastair, whilst washing dishes, came up with the idea of floating glass over tin.

In 1952 a small development plant was erected known as a Pilot Plant. This was at our Rolled Plate factory in connection with our Sheet Glass Works at St Helens.

As the Pilot Plant was being fed from a production line, it was decided to work on a shift system 24 hours per day, so that the experiment was covered by one foreman and three men per shift — all glassmakers.

The foremen were responsible for the glass and working conditions required by the Research and Development Department, such as the width, thickness, temperatures, speeds and all hot work controls.

During the period of development work on the float line Pilot Plant there were plenty of jobs in and around the St Helens area, which was a good thing for Pilkington, because experimental failures and success were not being talked about by the media, which ultimately helped in the secrecy of float glass development.

It was during the float pilot experiments that some of the workmen who were good, loyal, hardworkers, were being noticed by senior management. The workmen who were furnace workers sensed this observation by management and this gave them hopes for the future, which gave them enthusiasm, into trying and even suggesting any new ideas to assist the experiments.

The Plate Glass Works at Doncaster, played a major role in the early experimental days of the Float process, by making the first saleable product known as Vitrolite, 1957-58 and afterwards several members of their teams came to assist us at St. Helens.

3

SIR ALASTAIR PILKINGTON

Many a time people have said to me "You worked with Alastair Pilkington for many years, what was your impression of him?"

Well, first of all he was a very well educated, self-willed and a shy man, who knew exactly where he was going and how he was going to get there.

When I say shy, he always gave me the impression he was shy at mixing with the working classes, but not with the higher ranks, so people may say snobby, but no, I honestly believe it was a real shyness because I know as a workman I could more or less say anything to him within sense and reason, and he would discuss things with me, but I had more opportunities than most other shop floor workers to talk to him and understand his nature, and it was because of this shyness and work pressures, he seemed to have forgotten the needs of the shop floor worker.

Yet, in a sense this could be understood, just like the captain of a big ship, steering it through mountainous seas, and leaving the catering of the passengers to the officers on the lower decks, this is my opinion of what exactly Alastair was doing, putting yesterdays behind him and thinking of the tomorrow.

The reason I mention the word shyness of the working class is because I personally know of many occasions when Alastair could have been very annoyed with different shop floor people, and could have retaliated verbally, as a snob would have done, but he always kept a quiet council of his own. Also, I really don't remember any social function or occasion when he joined in with the shop floor people for a good chat and a drink.

To be honest I think in some respects he felt uncomfortable with the shop floor worker.

My first summing up of Alastair was way back in 1948 when working with him at Doncaster. He was the perfect gentleman, never cross questioning anything I said or did.

I remember one day quite clearly when we were having our lunch together in the foreman's office at Doncaster. We were discussing the difference in the Danum Hotel and the Reindeer Hotel, for Alastair was staying there at the time and what amused me was when Alastair said "I had kippers for breakfast but I was really put off enjoying them". In my best English manners I asked, "Why Mr Pilkington?" He said there was a young lady sat opposite him showing her bare knees, which was disgraceful at a breakfast table. "Oh" I said, I didn't say anything else, but being a good gentleman I nearly asked him if he wanted to change hotels, but I didn't. I kept the thought to myself and then wondered at the time if he was pulling my leg or was it his shy way.

There have been odd occasions in the early development days when I had a little bet with him on some float glass making move or other. The bet was never above one penny. No, he wasn't a betting man, but on that type of challenge, I could sense a shyness he was guiding himself away from.

In 1964 when the second licensee float line was starting up for Libbey-Owens-Ford in California, we had many problems with big bath bubbles, as a matter of fact, the whole ribbon of glass was similar to one big sheet of marbles.

The Vice President of Libbey-Owens-Ford, Henry Dodge, better known as Hank, was Pilkington's best ally. I am sure we had no other friend in the world as good as him who was always there when needed.

Hank was living in the Ambassador Motel in Stockton, the same hotel as us and one night he walked into the bar at about 10 p.m. (as he did every night) and said, "Eh Tommy, what is that song about bubbles?" So of course we all started singing 'I'm forever blowing bubbles'.

Hank, after a few drinks said: "I am going to ring Alastair Pilkington to waken him up, as it will by now be 5.00am English time, to let him know the position out here." We asked Hank what he was going to say? He replied: "I am going to sing to him 'I'm forever blowing bubbles' over the phone."

Alastair came over to America the following day. I could see he was a little baffled with the situation but being the very busy man he was, he made some technical decisions and left his Technical and Production Manager to follow the changes through and returned to England the following day.

Before he left I was walking down the side of the lehr with him, I could see he was worried so I said: "You know, Alastair, if the Americans cannot accept a few marbles for a while, well, they do not deserve the float process". He smiled and said: "Yes, that's right."

But never once did he show any signs of being worried to the shop floor workmen or blame them for any slight mistake, he kept all his battles upstairs. Yes, he was a technical man first and last.

For many years Alastair was in and out of work at all times of the day and night, as development changes and recommendations were required.

There was always a 9 a.m., 4 p.m. and 9 p.m. meeting everyday to discuss progress. Alastair attended and chaired everyone of them for at least the first four years on the production line at Cowley Hill Works.

In those days he came to work in a mackintosh. He would come approximately ½ hour before each meeting time, have a walk around the process so that he would have his own briefing ready for discussion in the meetings. He always kept strictly to his own technical side of the job. For example, I never saw Alastair interfere with a workman's job. He was definitely a technical glassmaker and not a manual glassmaker, at the time there was a shortage of both, and I am sure Alastair knew this.

After noting little incidents of workmen shyness, my final one was approximately two years ago.

One Saturday morning there were a number of V.I.P.'s and glass technologists visiting Pilkington to view the float process.

Before the works visit Alastair was in the canteen explaining to the visitors about the float glass invention and the early problems we encountered.

At the end there was a question period and as some of the people were asking questions I was amazed when Sir Alastair openly said: "Well, Tommy Grundy, one of your guides at the back, can answer that question, maybe better than I can," which happened on a few questions. I gave the answers but I also knew Alastair knew the answers as well as I did, if not better. Once again this gave me proof that he was not a snob. He respects what has been done by men like myself to help in the float glass success. Now he has stepped so high up the ladder it would be practically impossible for him to repair the bottom rung without damaging the centre and upper rungs, which the shareholders would not tolerate because of profits.

When I think in terms of technical inventions, yes Alastair was brilliant, but the man who invented the wheel never had the real answer as to how many men it would need to turn it, or what size of an engine was required to move it, but still at the same time we cannot take away the brilliance of thinking from the inventor and I believe this contributed a little to his shop floor shyness, because of the abnormal amount of hard work and technical knowledge that was necessary to be absorbed by the glassmaker in the progress of the float invention.

Now with the university educated technical people I believe he was not shy because he knew that they had been educated and fully trained to cope with his demands in technical glassmaking and they were being paid accordingly with accelerated promotions in sight.

Alastair was also a very brilliant industrialist in technology, in sales and industrial politics, but of course, he had the finest tutors in the glass world in the Pilkington family, and with a man like Lord Harry Pilkington behind him at the time, he was brilliant enough to take full advantage of his suggestions and help.

Ultimately every glass manufacturer in today's world wants to shake hands with Alastair Pilkington and licence his invention which, for world prestige for Pilkington, is excellent and more so for the shareholder.

I remember one day when the Queen had lunch in the St. Helens Town Hall, Alastair was invited and I was a St. Helens councillor at the time, so my wife and myself were invited to lunch as well.

Whilst waiting for the Queen's arrival before lunch was served, all guests were in an ante-room, chatting over pre-dinner drinks for half an hour. I saw Sir Alastair chatting with one of the councillors for quite a long time. I knew I could have gone over to him and had a chat but somehow or other I felt a little shy and inferior. I know this maybe hard to explain to some people, yet on the other hand I feel sure he saw me.

After lunch, Alastair and myself met in the foyer, he was waiting for the works car to pick him up to take him to Head Office.

The car was late and Alastair and myself entered into a great discussion about Pilkington building a float glass line in Sweden.

I wanted to know why we were building more float lines in other countries instead of in St. Helens. Of course, naturally Sir Alastair went through all the pros and cons of trade policies and I was putting the emphasis on jobs for the people of St. Helens.

He listened very carefully and patiently and gave me a good clear answer to each of my questions. What I didn't know was that four years later Greengate, St. Helens, known as UK5, would be starting up as a float glass line.

Alastair and myself are of similar age, we were both in the forces during the 1939-45 war, unfortunately Alastair was taken prisoner on Crete.

He joined Pilkington in 1947 and we worked together in 1948.

I am sure as the years progressed especially 1948 to the 1960's, each of us had a little knowledge, e.g. me practical, him technical in glassmaking, which working as part of a team was vital to the float glass success, but Sir Alastair was the inventor and the ship's captain.

I sincerely wish him every happiness in his retirement.

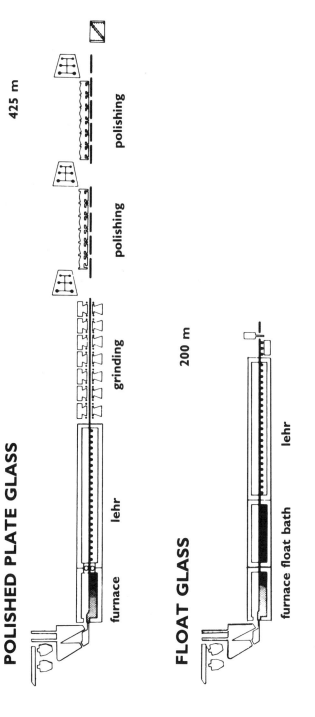

POLISHED PLATE GLASS

425 m

furnace   lehr   grinding   polishing   polishing

FLOAT GLASS

200 m

furnace   float bath   lehr

Comparison of stages in the polished plate glass process and in the float glass process.

20

4

FLOAT IS BORN

In 1955 Pilkington decided to risk building a full scale production unit for float glass further development at Cowley Hill Works. Because we were now changing the scene from plate glass manufacture to float glass manufacture I would like to change the name from furnace to casting machine and lehr which were the furnace man's responsibility on the Float Line.

It was decided to rebuild and convert No. 1 Line into a float line.

For this purpose the furnace was redesigned. With a casting machine and a float bath, and then a different design of annealing lehr, that was our first float production line set up.

As the line was being designed and built, the float line personnel were being chosen on ability, service and potential.

With my experiences and being a Foreman at the time I was chosen to be the Senior Foreman of the float line. We still had a plate glass line working so it was a matter of splitting up the experienced foremen as money still had to be made with plate glass production, which meant a big intake of new unskilled workers for both lines.

As was stated earlier it became a task of the "non skilled" training "non skilled", because at this time there were no training sections for glassmakers, and the men had to use a lot of common sense and discretion to help them with their jobs.

Senior Management were very few and had plenty of work

outside the scope of the workmen, in many administration jobs which they had to do on their own, are now split up among more people today.

It was because of work pressures that a good working relationship and trust in job resulted between management and worker in good glassmaking.

The Research and Development departments could not help us with our new glassmaking problems because they were not glassmakers as practice required.

Research and Development were very busy with their own work of which there were still many unsolved problems of float development of their own.

It was in March 1957 when the recruitment for more non-skilled workers began, which also meant the start of a job upgrading for many men. This was a risk that had to be taken, e.g. in some cases some men were promoted to charge-hands and foremen who had little practical experience for the positions required.

Fortunately at Cowley Hill Works there were three wise men in control (1) the Works Manager, Ken Earle had a good quiet, well mannered, experienced way of encouraging all to give their best, he had a strong belief in charity beginning at home, (2) the Production Manager, Ernie Litherland, was a down to earth excellent glassmaker for both Production and Development Projects. Yes he called a spade a spade, and fully understood the hearts of the glassmakers. When the glassmakers were depressed or tired he would say, have a break, go for a pint of beer and come back refreshed to start again, which everyone appreciated, and (3) the Float Line Manager, Celfyn Thomas, who was a brilliant engineer, developer, worker and encourager; in fact he gave everything a man could give to a job, the glassmakers would go through fire or water for him.

These three people were even in a new extra field of work themselves, and had many more administration problems, many more technical problems, more work people to organise etc, which meant more responsibilities unimaginable previously.

The trust the Senior Management had in the workmen was impeccable.

The preparation for warming up the float line was entirely new to past practices, we had new constructional designs, new maintenance methods, different materials, new chemistry, new safety aspects, new types of instructions, new types of people with new ideas.

Some of the glassmakers were experiencing for the first time the dangers of hot molten tin, burnt town's gas, electrical equipment, and induction heating.

At this stage the plan was to let the glass flow from the furnace, through the casting rollers to set the width and thickness of the glass and then into the float bath to be fire finished and next into the lehr to be annealed.

It was noticeable there were experts in various development design areas, but when all had put their pieces where they wanted, it was still like a jig-saw puzzle. Someone had to put all the pieces together to complete the picture and this so happened to be the glassmaker's job which physically and mentally was the hardest at the time.

We had planned to start up at 8.00 am on 8.5.57 and for approximately one week before start up the shopfloor workers had been working plenty of hot, hard overtime; but the difference between this float line start-up and a plate glass start-up was we all had to do similar work as for a normal plate glass start — plus. And I mean a massive plus, with the warming up of the bath, then filling it with molten tin, setting the bath refractories in position with a hot pressurised gaseous atmosphere blasting at the glassmaker each time he opened up the bath, and having to clean all the tin oxide out of the bath before start-up.

On the morning of start-up my job as Senior Foreman glassmaker began at 6.00 am with other glassmakers working overtime. We began by checking all around the float line to make sure all temperatures were on target, all equipment was in working order. Every glassmaker was briefed about his expectation in case of emergencies.

When the Foremen and myself were satisfied everything was ready I reported to my Manager and he told me to go ahead and start-up the line.

This was the moment the men had been waiting for.

After a final check-up I gave the order to lift up the gate or tweel and the glass began to flow to the casting machine, then when the glass came on the hot tin and the men began to assist the glass over the tin surface this was the beginning of the first float production line.

We had a hard struggle to get the hot glass through the bath

23

simply because we did not know enough about the temperatures, chemistry and conditions required for a float bath at that time.

When we did manage to feed the glass from the Float Bath to the annealing lehr we were in trouble again, because we were in a new field of float glass annealing conditions we hadn't expected, and after a period of approximately one hour of struggling with hot broken glass, and tin oxide dross, we stopped the line, so we could clear away the broken glass, discuss our unexpected problems, and most important, give the glassmakers a rest for they were all absolutely exhausted with sweating and removing broken glass.

The glassmakers had to cope with four major forces together, (a) the furnace feeding machine had to be readjusted, (b) the casting machine in the float bath had to be reset, (c) the float bath had to be cleaned up and sealed up, and (d) the annealing lehr had to be cleaned out.

This was a testing time for the glassmakers. It was the beginning of teamwork, which I doubt will ever be equalled again by shop floor workers.

The men on the furnace began using discretion and taking the responsibility of doing extra, so that the senior people could help at the float bath end and this type of teamwork began, and carried on and wherever help was needed no matter how hard or dangerous, or hot the job was, if the men could possibly do it there was no such thing as a demarcation line (marvellous team spirit).

I believe this job attitude was a key factor in the early days of the float glass success.

I must emphasise at this point the size of our plans for alterations did include engineers, electricians, builders, etc., but when they had done their job as in many instances, it was then left to the glassmakers and the development departments.

It was on this first day of production trial when we were trying 1000 tons of glass per week, compared to 75 tons per week on a pilot line that the glassmaking people began to realise that they all had to do a lot of research and development work in many ways, especially in their own minds.

(1)   Because of many hours overtime and dirty sweaty clothes, home and family life was becoming upset.

24

(2) The glassmakers were becoming workaholics.

(3) We had to be very careful about the dangers of hot molten tin and learn about it, not only for glassmaking purposes, but for personnel safety as well.

(4) The controlling and reaction of gases (still experimental). Personnel safety was a priority.

(5) The dangers and sums for electrical heating (still experimental).

At this stage little was known about the combined effects with glass, but the glassmaker was always in the front line of battle with float glass making, for the float line was always under his supervision and control.

We started the line up again at about 3.00 pm the same day and managed to establish a ribbon of glass through the float bath into the annealing lehr. It was decided to leave well alone and let the job settle down, so the glassmakers could have a well earned rest, and for further study of the process by the development department.

The problems of the glass were mostly chemical problems, because of a condensation of tin and tin compound depositing on the water cooled casting rollers which were being imprinted in the glass surfaces, also heavy dross was accumulating on the tin surface.

It was decided after a few months of non saleable glass that something desperate had to be done because of finance, and breathing time for a new progress study, so it was decided to make rough cast glass through the float bath which had to be ground and polished.

Making rough cast glass was another new experience the glassmakers had to confront, because although we had advanced a little with conditions in a float bath, our main problem came in the annealing lehr, in setting the correct stresses and strains for grinding and polishing and again hard work and thoughtful thinking and overtime was required by the shop floor glassmakers because glass production was still their baby.

After a few weeks of plate glass working through the float bath it was decide to shut the line down and reorganise the float bath design to try again without a casting machine at a later date.

Some of the problems we had to encounter during the first sessions were: when many times iron bars had to be used to remove the thick coats of dross from the tin surface; refractories had to be removed from the bath roof; bath bottom refractories came floating up and had to be removed; occasionally we would encounter a tin leak. All these problems created hot hard heavy overtime work, and many-a-time dangerous work. These were added jobs to the glassmakers' world and even new to the development world.

On the furnace side we had the changeover from producer gas to oil firing, plus the new uses of platinum covered refractories was also new to the glassmakers.

Putting it all in a nutshell the shop floor glassmakers were becoming technical glassmakers but learning the skills in a practical trial and error way.

As the Senior Foreman practical glassmaker I had to work hard and learn, and set an example with my standards of growing technical knowledge. I could not fail to notice how the Foremen and some of the workers really got down to the task of learning the technical aspects of development work which was a well needed asset at this time.

As a matter of interest the danger of tin leaks was one of our big problems, because hot tin is very dangerous and if water got under the tin and the steam is trapped under the tin then the tin would explode which it did happen a couple of times, but we had to explain to the Fire Brigade how to tackle tin leaks because their first reaction was always to put a water hose pipe on anything hot, instead of using chemicals. We did occasionally drain the tin out of the bath which was a dangerous procedure.

After a pause of a few months the float line started up again but this time without a casting machine. Once again the glassmakers were beginning to experience new designs which meant new problems and new techniques.

The bath was changed over from tin induction heating to bath roof electrical heating; the bath atmosphere was changed from burnt town's gas to a mixture of Nitrogen and Hydrogen.

Instead of a fixed thickness and fixed width ribbon of glass coming to the float bath, we had a 40 inch wide refractory spout, which the glass flowed down onto molten tin. This then had to be temperature controlled to make the width required.

This new set up was in its experimental stage and once again the glassmakers had to bear the brunt of the hard experimental, pratical work, because at every change of any description the men actually did the pratical job, under all types of conditions, because the float line was the glassmakers' responsibility. This

26

was something definite we could not shirk.

The Development job was to bring forward ideas and theories; ours was to prove or disprove them in practice. Glassmakers were responsible for the whole line 24 hours a day and as a continuous stream of glass came at us day after day, month after month, holidays or time off became a thing of the past.

When we started up with a refractory spout lip the front of the bath was wide open and as the men were controlling the hot glass onto the hot tin at 1000°C, the hot atmosphere gases and the flames from the spout burners made the area where the men were working unbearable.

Once again the men had the problems when rowing the glass through the bath, which was 80 feet long, as the glass was just not hot enough by the time it reached the end of the bath, and, it was breaking as we tried to put it on the lehr rollers. When we did eventually put the glass onto the lehr rollers then there was a transmission pull pulling the glass from the spout over the tin surface to the lehr.

The next job was to seal up the float bath, because we had changed to a spout lip. The next hard hot job was the fitting of the refractory restrictor tiles in the tin under the lip to restrict the glass flow. This was another hot tiring job which needed experience and skills.

At the exit end of the bath there was always cold glass, and plenty of tin dross, which all had to be cleaned away.

Next in the lehr where we had cold broken glass it had to be cleaned out.

The number of jobs were unbelievable.

A start-up programme was something I used to try and write out for e.g. if we were due to start up 8.00 a.m. my progress chart would be:

Glassmakers' responsibilities:-
7.00 a.m. Check on furnace temperature targets, materials, tools etc.
Check on spout temperature targets and spout conditions and refractories.
Check on bath tin temperature target.
Check on tin and bath condition targets.
Check on bath electrical heaters targets.
Check on the atmosphere gases and flow.
Check on bath tools and materials.

Check on lehr temperatures and tools.

Check on all drives, cooling systems, emergency systems etc.

7.45 a.m. If all was O.K. would have a meeting and everyone would be briefed about his expectations during the start up and settling down period.

If in doubt about anything the start-up time would be delayed until everything was ready. Yes I was the senior practical man and it was my job and I could not afford to take any risks which could result in personnel accidents or plant mishaps.

Many-a-time when there were problems in the float bath and the problem was becoming unmanageable, the glassmaker, either myself or the shift foreman, had the authority to stop the glass from going into the float bath, and use discretion to save plant and materials.

The drill would be:

(a) Lower the tweel to stop hot glass entering the spout and bath (set burners to keep nice temperature).

(b) Take coolers and guide fences out of the bath.

(c) Row all the remaining glass out of the bath, redistribute atmosphere gas N^2H^2.

(d) Seal up the bath to keep oxygen out.

(e) Set new temperature targets in the bath.

(f) Reset the lehr targets.

(g) Reset furnace targets and maybe withdraw furnace feeder.

The extra jobs involved a lot of sweating and overtime.

It was on occasions like these that the glassmakers needed a drink to keep them from collapsing with fatigue or dehydration. Tea and salt tablets were provided, but the majority needed a few beers to stop them going mad.

I know these men worked many hours even 12 or 16 hours at a time and in between, have six or seven pints of beer when convenient. As one man put it, it cost more for beer on these hot jobs than we got wages.

Everyday it was common to see someone shout out with cramp, mostly in the fingers and arms with the lifting of hot heavy bars, which we used in the bath for rowing the glass.

We did have protective clothing in the form of asbestos suits and asbestos gloves, clogs and sweat jerseys and eye protection in the bath area at all times; but in the conditions that were being encountered when working on start up and emergencies this heavy clothing was a weakness in itself.

I remember the jokes, when a glassmaker's wife did the washing, a clothes line was not needed, the clothes were so thick from sweat and salt that the clothes stood up for themselves, and when they did manage to get home the dog used to bite them, as it had forgot what they looked like.

With a spout lip we did progress with glass control and bath conditions, but during these periods many experiments were carried out and many theories put forward, most did not work when put to practice.

One of the main problems was the spout area, with the glass flows not working freely and in some places the glass was being held too long causing crystals to grow, which meant we had too many cold glass crystals in the ribbon of glass.

It was the glassmakers' job to prepare, warm up and install different sizes of restrictor tiles in the hot tin around the spout, to see the changes in glass flows as the development people requested.

Everything the development department requested was done to the best of the men's ability but with theory after theory not working. Naturally, we were allowed to put forward some of the men's suggestions but still we didn't seem to be getting any further apart from small temporary improvements.

During this period the Research and Development and glassmaking management held meetings every morning at 9.00 a.m. sometimes in the afternoon and then about 9.00 p.m. to discuss results and put forward new theories. (I did attend most of these meetings and I believe a stage had been reached where everyone concerned began clutching at straws to solve the crystal problem).

We had a stroke of luck by a mistake which was hidden at the time.

As result of the late evening meetings many a job was done by no-one else only the glassmakers in attendance, and with our workload being so great we had a drink at 10.00 p.m. then went back to work, this was a type of concession that was allowed and happened regularly otherwise the men would have not worked all the overtime that was required.

One night, we were fitting a refractory behind the spout lip and squeezing the refractory in position with a long hot iron bar when the bar slipped and cracked the spout, but at the time we did not realise how important it was, because we had raised the spout lip so much on many occasions, changing tiles and the spout was well worn.

This released the crystals and changed the glass flow which proved later to be valuable to glassmaking.

When the Senior Management came in next morning and noticed a difference in the glass they were happy, because the glass was saleable: the crystal particles had moved from the centre and insides of the ribbon to the extreme edges of the ribbon, which was a great asset to saleable width, when everything else was alright.

With the spout being broken the line was shut down. Hot work again.

A new spout lip was installed. Also, several alterations were made around the bath area to assist the bath sealing.

The setting up of the new spout and starting the glassmaking again, was exactly the same, hot, hard work, with plenty of overtime again.

We had crystals again in the centre and edges of the ribbon. Many theories were carried out, the glassmakers were continually changing hot refractory to different positions, but all we got was browned off with sweat.

Having a trial like this one was good for us, because as time was going on the glassmakers were getting more experience and confidence in the new technical methods of modern glassmaking. As the old story goes, the man who has to work hard and sweat when mistakes are made, is very observant for future mistakes, which gives him the ability to learn faster than the man who can walk away and read, or think up another way.

The foremen and some of the workmen were being proved brilliant in their understanding and handling of the characteristics of tin, the calculations of electric heating in measurements of kilowatt, the distribution, safety calculation of atmosphere gases N^2H^2, using instruments for checking both pressures and developing float line safety new glassmaking conditions; and most important personnel safety.

One important point I must mention, the firm were very lucky because a large portion of men such as foremen came out of the forces having been N.C.O's in the Army, Petty Officers in the Navy, Navigators in Bomber Command, but unfortunately for them, they had no pieces of paper to say they had 'O' Levels, 'A'

Levels etc., or any industrial tradesmen credentials or apprenticeship. This automatically put them on the lowest grades of pay when they joined industry as glassmakers and this label stayed with them at pay packet level.

These assets were used in the development work, and taken for granted as the glassmakers contribution.

It was revealed in the studies of glass flows in models, that a hotter freer flow was needed to discourage the crystals from forming in the spout, and it was revealed the need to build a spout which incorporated characteristics of the broken one which had a sag in it.

We started up again with a new design of spout lip, similar to the one which had a sag in it, this gave every encouragement because the crystals had moved from the centre and inside positions of the ribbon to the extreme edges, which would ultimately give a wider saleable width.

Next we had problems with the tin oxide deposits, and the emphasis was to seal up the bath and aim for a good high bath pressure to keep out the oxygen, but what was really happening when we got high bath pressure was a little baffling.

Because the chemistry was not quite correct at the time, it caused a lot of tin oxide to deposit on the bath refractories and also on the glass surfaces and this prevented us from producing saleable glass.

Many types of theories were tried out, without success.

With working around the spout area a lot we noticed that each time we opened up there was a deposit of tin oxide which quickly built up especially where we made a small gap, and there was a pressure leak of atmosphere gas gushing through the gap.

The glassmakers checked up with the glass quality and we noticed each time this happened, the tin oxide deposits on the glass surface were greatly reduced even to the extent the glass was saleable for this type of fault, of course, this was against the chemical physics theoretically.

As regards to the thickness of the glass, we were fortunate to find that the glass settled down to 6.5 mm thickness once it settled on the tin and there was a market for 6.5 mm glass.

Another problem was the ribbon width control, which with trial and error on both technical and practical sides was overcome.

Next there was the ribbon control to keep it in a straight line, whilst it was going through the bath, into the lehr, this was another hard task of trial and error which eventually the glassmakers won.

It was 1958 the breakthrough to saleable glass was made, but even then we had not overcome all the problems.

The glassmakers still had to work many hours hard sweating overtime, for it was a matter of keeping our fingers crossed that nothing would go wrong, but many times it did, owing to lack of technical knowledge for we were still in the development stage.

Although saleable glass was being made, and everything was still in the development stage, Pilkington decided to announce the invention of float glass to the world.

Friday 23rd January 1959 (already spent £4 million).

News of the invention was revealed by Sir Harry Pilkington to more than 70 journalists at the Royal Society of Arts in John Adam St, London.

This is a great occasion for us said Sir Harry proudly as he opened the proceedings.

Simultaneously Mr Douglas Phelps, chairman of the executive board of Pilkington Brothers, was giving information to the joint industrial council at St Helens.

We believe we can claim float glass to be the most fundamental revolutionary and important of all the advances in glass making of the present century.

After nearly seven years of intensive work, on a large scale, an entirely new method of making flat glass has been developed by us at St Helens.

The process is fully patented and we think it will ultimately be used all over the world.

We have called it the float process and the glass will be known as float glass.

The essential point of the new process he said, is a continuous ribbon of glass floating on a bath of molten metal with a brilliant natural finish, which will eliminate the grinding and polishing required for the manufacture of plate glass.

In appearance the float glass combines the best qualities of both plate and sheet glass. The quantity now being produced is quite considerable but not enough for it to be offered freely.

Float was the only experimental method tried in the firm's attempt to keep a lead, other lines of attack had to be abandoned. The price of progress was not only the cost of successful development but of failures too.

In plate glass we have been the principle inventors of most of the revolutionary advances of the century. We have willingly paid the heavy price because we know that, more expensive than to lead in industry is to be led.

The chairman said any new phases of the new process would be discussed with the unions. He also paid tribute to those who had helped to keep the process a well kept secret.

When a big plant was being run, continuously, a way had to be found of using the production when it became good enough to sell, and one had to be sure it was good enough to be of value to the users.

Pilkington approached long standing friends, Triplex, and confided in Sir Graham Cunningham. With a friendliness and co-operation which the firm was proud to acknowledge, Triplex agreed to accept float glass in the manufacture of safety glass.

It had been proved that very strict standards could be met by float and that the firm's biggest single customer had confidence in the new product.

This announcement was a booster to the morale of the men on the float line but at the same time, it put a massive responsibility onto everyone of them, it was amazing to see team work at its best.

If there was a problem on any of the three sections, Tank, Bath, or Lehr, that would affect saleable glass, the men would sweat, work overtime or anything necessary to help each other in their needs at work, irrespective of position or pay rate.

As time went on and we were becoming more efficient at making saleable glass, the signal for change was beginning to ring.

Some managers and work people in the Grinding and Polishing departments also the Warehousing, Cutting and Inspection and even sales people began saying float glass would not be as good a product as plate glass.

We on the float line were fighting hard for them to accept float glass and the controversy came to a head when Alastair Pilkington decided to set up an exhibition of a number of large sheets of glass, some from the float Bath and some that had been ground and polished from the plate glass line.

Leading examination experts from Quality Control, salesmen and others were invited to examine and comment on which was float glass and which was plate glass.

Well, as sure as they all were, it was found the majority of examiners could not identify float from plate, so this gave the float line men a bigger encouragement to battle on with the float process, but at this stage we could only produce 6.5 mm thickness of which thickness there was a demand for.

The next problem was the making of thinner glasses.

For this purpose all types of theories and known practices were put forward and tried, and again, plenty of sweating, hard work and overtime being worked by all; it was very hard to find the correct temperature conditions, and the glass was either too hot or too cold, which created many shutdowns.

Because we were trying to make thinner glasses, heavier equipment for cooling the glass was being used. Edge roll machines were being tried for the first time ever, new distribution patterns of electrical heating and new distributions of atmosphere gases were being tried, it was just like starting all over again.

The Foremen and men accepted and tried every suggestion that was put forward by development department and some were successful and some failed, but that was not good enough. Team work at this stage was needed more than ever and many good ideas were put forward by the workmen, who by now had gained a lot of valuable practical working knowledge of conditions required in a float bath and it was because of their loyalty and enthusiasm for the success of float many of their suggestions were made to work, which ultimately was a big contribution to the production of thinner glasses, still not yet mastered.

Pilkington built a new and bigger float line which was to produce double the production as No. 1 line, this was known as No. 3 line.

It was in May 1961 when, as the foundations for this line were being laid, the Queen and Duke of Edinburgh were invited to come along and see the float process.

At that time we were still having a lot of problems with glassmaking. Everyday was a hard sweating day for the glassmakers, as a matter of fact they were absolutely physically exhausted but none would give up and lie down, for the news of the Royal visit was a big uplift to them, and their families.

The Royal visit meant a lot of extra work with the spit and polish and cleaning around the float line.

As for myself, it was a massive strain for me, because a few weeks before the visit, I was informed by the Works Manager that I was being formally introduced to the Queen and the Duke.

The day before the visit I was on the float line from 6.00 a.m. until midnight and I went home absolutely exhausted, hoping and praying that everything would go well for the visit. I don't think I slept one full hour owing to tiredness and excitement.

Because of the nature of the work, and long hours being worked there was one Landlord who always had his back door open and the men could go in for a drink anytime of the night or day. Boy he must have made a fortune after closing hours.

It was a fact, around the first couple of years of float development at Cowley Hill that if there was any emergency on the line and men had to be called in work, no way was the van driver to go to a man's home without he had checked up at the pub first (The White Horse).

One chap came into work one shift with a black eye because the van driver made a mistake of not checking up properly on a thirsty man, who was dead tired and thirsty after approximately 12 or 16 hours sweating; for after his first pint he fell fast asleep, too tired to go home.

When he did eventually arrive home, his wife was very upset and worried as to where he had been, he said at work. She gave him a black eye, and said that will teach you a lesson to come home instead of going to the "White Horse".

The wives and families of some of the men must have been real angels to put up with the problems of the days. For I am absolutely sure, a lot of false courage and discussions by the men when having a pint ot two, was one of the biggest hidden assets of the float process.

It was in 1961 that No. 4 continuous grinder was shut down and the writing was obvious to the glassmakers that new men were coming into the department to be trained up in readiness for the new float line; this did release the work pressure temporarily but, the important point was, the only people who could train them were foremen training foremen and workmen training each other for there were no other people competent enough to train them in the types of jobs they were required for.

The plate glass line was still working and some of the Foremen and men who had been called upon to work overtime with the float line men when, there were emergencies, had to train some of the new intake in their respective jobs, as well, so that the transfer could be more efficient when the new float line was ready for commissioning. This meant at that time there would be two float glass lines and one plate glass line working at the same time.

The new float line was started up 19 March, 1962.

Approximately one month before start up the teams of foremen and workmen were sorted out so that experience was put where it was needed most, which ultimately meant new types of responsibility was being showered on to some of the men quicker than they had ever dreamed of.

I am sure no College or University could have taught them the things like the points about molten tin, atmosphere gases, electrical heating, machine calculations, temperature require- ments, all the things required for float glass making and, most important, the safety of personnel and plant and equipment, in the short time they had to learn.

Once again, it was overtime and hard sweating for the men and foremen on the new line as well as the other line for they were still having their problems.

It was a start up to remember.

The day we were to start up the line, the men were really tired because we had been working preparing a larger furnace, a larger bath, and a larger lehr with many new problems, and heavier equipment. We were once again in a big green field with the Directors looking for greater expectations more quickly than before, and the men were saying thank God we are starting up today.

My job as Senior Foreman on the new line, was to do as No. 1 line, check everything was ready, e.g. hot glass conditions on target, float bath conditions ready, lehr conditions ready, plant and equipment ready. Explain to the foremen and workmen the start-up procedure and what was expected from them, from experiences gained on No. 1 line. When I was satisfied I would tell the Manager I was ready to start the line up and he would give me the authority to go ahead.

It was 8a.m., 19th March, 1962, when I gave the signal to commence the glass flow from the furnace into the float bath. The glass from the furnace was in excellent condition, but, when the glass was in the float bath we then realised we were in a new ball game, with tin and glass temperatures, owing to the size of the bath, which was a new adventure to us, for No. 1 float bath was 100ft. long and 10ft. wide. No. 3 bath was 150 ft. long and 15ft. wide and by the time the glass got rowed to the exit and off the bath the glass was very cold and breaking.

The bath began to fill quickly with cold glass, so we had to stop the glass flow from the furnace, but unfortunately there was a mechanical fault on the control tweel, and by the time the glass was finally stopped from coming out of the furnace, we had cold glass approximately four inches thick all over the tin surface.

It took the foremen and workmen approximately 30 hours to clean out the cold glass using sledge hammers and chiselbars,

*A typical
Hot End
worker.*

working under atrocious conditions, because of the heat and the pressurised H^2N^2 atmospheric conditions which were necessary to prevent too much oxidisation of tin.

Yes, casualties like cramp, burns, scalds, headaches and fatigue were now being accepted as normal by these men.

It was approximately 2a.m. on the 21st when I decided to have another try at starting the glass flowing through the float bath again. We were all really tired but the Foremen and men were prepared to give their everything, and after a long hard hot struggle we managed to row the glass through the float bath into the annealing lehr. Only God knows how we all managed to survive all the hard, hot sweating overtime, and at the same time keep control of our other responsibilities, it was miraculous.

For example, after start-up I went home and slept for a few hours, and then back into work again for there was still a lot of hot work to finish, to settle the plant down to working target, things like sealing the bath, setting refractories in hot tin, cleaning up tin dross, which all needed experienced practical attention, by the Foremen and men, and then I still had my administration duties to attend to with personnel, plant and glassmaking functions to see to.

Now that we had two float lines working the foremen and men were really being overworked, because of the newness of the process. Each time there was trouble on any line we helped each other out with hot work and overtime. There were never any complaints because the men battled on with high hopes set on the future of their jobs and families and Pilkingtons.

As time went by, it was noticeable once again how the foremen and men were putting into practice little suggestions and ideas of their own to improve their working environment, which ultimately helped in better sealing, better ribbon control in the float bath, better types of tools for rowing the glass etc. little things which helped to stabilise conditions all along the float line which was a massive contribution to saleable glass.

5

ROYAL VISIT

It was a few weeks before the visit of the Queen and Duke of Edinburgh that I received a confidential letter from Mr Earle the Cowley Hill Works manager, informing me that I was to be formally introduced to the Queen and Duke when they came to visit the Float Glass Line at Cowley Hill on May 15th 1961.

At that time I was asked to keep it private and confidential, which I did, to the effect that it became very embarrassing for me at home, because although I had told my wife I had to wait nearer to the occasion before I could tell my daughter and my son, who were working at Pilkingtons.

My daughter came home from work many a time and she would be really upset and say, such a person and his wife had been invited to the works for the Queen's visit, why don't you ask them why my Mam can't come in to the works.

I did tell her eventually even before it was announced officially, that her Mam was being allowed in the works to stand at the front of the float line to see me being introduced to the Queen. As a matter of fact it was not easy to keep anything like that away from your children.

The Royal Visit was a great incentive to all at Pilkington, for extra people were employed, planning routes, making special stands, cleaning up places that hadn't seen a brush for years, the painters were painting here there and everywhere, no-one dare stand still for a minute otherwise someone with a paint brush would paint them. The shops in St Helens did plenty of trade with the red white and blue ribbons and Union Jacks as the flags were called in those days.

Three days before the visit we had some problems on the float bath and I think the works manager Mr Earle must have only had at the most four hours out of each 24, out of the factory, for the float needed a lot of extra attention at this crucial early stage and the float glassmakers were really tired but having said that, the Royal Visit was a massive uplift to the men and their families, and it came as an unexpected morale bonus just at the time it was needed. Everyone was happy and thrilled about the Royal Visit.

I suppose all the directors were happy, but on edge as well, that everything would go well on the day for they were all being introduced to the Queen and Duke. Oh boy I think there was more prayers said in Pilkington on the 24th May 1961 than at any other time in any one day in the history of the firm.

At precisely 10.28 a.m. on may 25th 1961 a great cheer went up as the Royal Standard was proudly hoisted above Cowley Hill Works, that was the moment when the gleaming Royal car with the reigning sovereign entered the works.

The Queen and Duke of Edinburgh stepped from the car, and shook hands with the Mayor of St Helens and Sir Harry Pilkington.

This was the first time the Queen had visited a Pilkington Glass Works, but the Duke had already visited other Pilkington factories at St Asaph in 1957 and Possilpark Glasgow in 1960.

The Royal Party which included Lord and Lady Derby was shown the plate glass process and then the float glass process.

This was the first time that anyone outside the firm had seen the whole of the secret process.

All the visitors wore safety spectacles in departments where there was a risk of eye injuries, including the Queen and the Duke, who wore tinted glasses.

The Royal party first saw diagrams illustrating the plate glass and the float glass process, then they viewed the excavation required for the new float line that was under construction and the Duke was impressed by the size of the excavation required to contain a modern glass tank.

Afterwards they visited the No. 4 plate glass tank, where they saw the raw materials being fed into the furnace, also the melting and forming ends of the process.

Because of the intense heat, special toughened glass screens had been erected to protect the Royal Party from the heat.

At the end of the plate glass tank the Queen and Duke saw a ribbon of molten glass 100 inches wide, leaving the casting machine and passing along on rollers through to the annealing lehr, and from the annealing lehr where it had been cooled in to the heads of the twin grinders, and then the polishing process.

Next came the float process. We who were on the float process had been nervously waiting for this moment, all hoping and praying everything would go well, without any of the unknown and known mishaps that could happen at any moment.

Every man was as clean and smart as the job allowed him to be, and I am sure if Pilkington had been selling mirrors to our men that morning they would have made a record sales profit, for every minute or so, someone would dash to the wash room to comb his hair, wash his hands, face, or something, and look in the mirror to see if he was smart enough, just in case the Queen wanted to shake hands or converse with them, some were nervous, some joking about it, and laughing. In a way it was good for morale because we had a different environment in the tank temporarily.

My manager Celfyn Thomas and myself were waiting at the entrance to the float line. We were both a little nervous ourselves, wondering about what questions we would be asked by the Queen and Duke and also how to address the Queen properly.

I said to Celfyn that I would be O.K. because they would ask him all the questions and then shake my hand and walk on, that is what I had a vision of.

The works policeman stationed at the entrance to the float line gave us the signal that the Royal Party were coming and being tired at the time, I think I was a little nervous.

Sir Harry came first with the Queen, and he introduced the manager who shook hands with he Queen, and then immediately, Sir Harry introduced me by name to the Queen and as I shook her hand, I replied, pleased to meet you Mam.

The Queen then asked me did I enjoy my work? I replied, Yes Mam, next the Queen asked how long had I been in the furnaces? I replied, since 1946 Mam. Then the Queen asked if I had been in the forces and which company had I served with? to which I replied, the Royal Engineers from 1939 to 1946 Mam.

By now the Queen's personality had made me feel quite

relaxed and comfortable and because of her smile and pleasant disposition I was smiling too. The Queen asked me if I worked at Pilkington's before I joined the forces? to which I replied, Yes Mam. Then she smiled and passed on into the float line.

Next came the Duke of Edinburgh who had been talking with Celfyn while the Queen was talking to me.

The Duke shook hands with me, smiled and passed on.

It was noticeable the Queen and Duke were moving along as near as possible to each other so the Queen does not keep the Duke waiting and vice versa.

As the Royal Party moved along the float line they were very impressed.

After visiting the float line the Queen and Duke spent some time inspecting a selection of the company's products and then signed the visitors book.

They left the exhibition, then the Royal Party watched a demonstration of glass cuttings, here the Duke smiled as he noticed a bandage on a finger of a cutter's mate, and said to the cutter's mate, "I expect I would cut myself too, if I tried to cut glass."

The came the grand climax of the Royal Visit. As the Queen and Duke left the works, they walked past 1,600 people who were on specially erected stands.

In the stands were directors' families, managers and wives, employees from Head Office, pensioners etc, and other St Helens workers.

The Queen and Duke greeted them with smiles and occasionally stopped to talk with pensioners and apprentices before getting into the car.

The Queen and Duke were driven through part of the works, past a stand to receive more hand clapping from 500 more pensioners and then along a route lined with 2,000 employees from Cowley Hill and City Road Works.

The Royal car then left the works through a new gate which by permission of Her Majesty has been named the Queens Gate in commemoration of the visit.

In 1961 pensioners meet the Queen.

6

FIRST LICENCEE

It was in 1962 that our first prospective licencees, P.P.G., came to Cowley Hill from America to see some of our float glass.

At this time the P.P.G. people were not allowed on the float bath but could only come to the end of No. 1 line which at that time was making 4 mm glass which they were very interested to see.

I remember they came to the end of the line approximately 10.00 a.m. and we were producing good glass, but while they were looking at the glass we had a catastrophe in the float bath. I sent a message to the Works Manager who was with them and he then took them to look at some samples in the warehouse without the licensees knowing what had happened.

We all knew it was a crucial time politically for Pilkington, I was determined to keep the glass moving as quickly as possible for the glass had broken at the exit end of the bath and had filled the bath, but out of sheer determination, hard work and sweat by the foremen and men we got the glass moving again.

During this period of approximately 45 minutes, the licensees were kept talking and looking at samples in the warehouse and when they came past the end of the line again, the glass was coming out as though nothing had happened, but the licensees were chaperoned quickly past, without examining the glass which was unsaleable at the time.

By now we had come a long way in understanding the

requirement needed to make good saleable 6.5 mm glass, but we were still in the development stage of producing thinner glasses, so the battle was still raging.

Pilkington had committed themselves to float glass and in November 1962 the No. 4 plate glass line was shut down which meant only float glass was being produced at Cowley Hill Works.

It had been decided to convert the Plate Glass Line into a float glass line with an output of 2,000 tons per week.

This was done by keeping the glass furnace, removing the first 140 ft. of the lehr, and putting a float bath in between the tank and the lehr and then extending and redesigning the lehr.

The Pilkington shop window was now in progress, for in 1961 two major developments were in progress, Research and Development headquarters at Lathom, and Head Office at Prescot Road.

Looking back now this period was the beginning of a new era in development, administration, and policy making, more academically minded people were being brought into the firm, and seeds were being sown for future expansion in departments like Personnel, Safety, Training, etc. but none of this affected the hard practical sweating side of the float glass making during this period, because the men we had were in the labouring market.

It was April 1963 when first we met the P.P.G training team leaders for discussions about their float glass training. Also at this time we had to train and prepare foremen and workmen for the conversion of the plate line that was due to start up in July 1963.

Owing to time and inexperience it was now proving that one of the major problems of float glass making was the organising, the training, and handling of the new float line glass workers, for at this time we had no qualified training department to assist us in this type of work, and we were still encountering in design, chemistry, practice and environment, new problems as we were progressing, which meant foreman training foreman, workman training workman, and of course team spirit a priority.

This was not easy for the men, because many were timid to the new dangers of hot tin, gases, electric etc. and examples of confidence were set by the more experienced men, especially in hot work. Also, the men were realising by now they were not just glassworkers but technically trained by each other as technical glassmakers; but without trade or academical qualifi-

45

cations, no one would accept them as such. This was also being noticed by the wives and families of the foremen and men, and many times it was said, it was the overtime pay which encouraged them, to stay with the job.

It was in early February 1963 that I was taken off the line to assist in the construction/conversion of the now known C.H. 4 line, also to plan the personnel workers and training schedules, for the heavy commitment approaching us; they were C.H. 4 start up, July 1963, training of the P.P.G. start-up team, June 1963, also Glaverbel of Belgium had signed up for a float licence and others were due to follow.

All this really meant we had to have enough trained foremen and men to work three float lines at Cowley Hill, and a minimum number of two teams of the most experienced trained foremen and men to be away at any one time for licensee start-up. Each start-up team required 16 people. What a marvellous set of men we had in the float line department who were always prepared under any stress or strain to do their best.

Once again I was given a major role in the responsibility for organisation and preparation for the C.H. 4 line conversion from the production side, and because of my hard work, experience and confidence and loyalty to the float process, many of my words and suggestions were being widely used by the Development, Engineering, Building and Production Department, but many things I put forward, many of them came to me over a period of time from the foremen and workmen.

I knew it had come to the repeat stage, we had to work many long hours at a time in preparation for a successful start-up.

By now I was getting tired and battle worn, but my Manager, Celfyn Thomas gave me plenty of help and confidence, by backing me up in discussions and requests from various departments.

The starting up of C.H. 4 line had to be a success, because by now we had two lots of licensees already signed up for the licensing of the float bath, and they had been invited to come along and see the start-up on 7th July 1963.

Once again, the foremen and men had to be moved around so experience was where it was most needed at the time, but, although they were getting tired of hot work and overtime, and practically no home life, their loyalty to float was still there.

On this occasion we had special wooden staging erected so

that our visitors could have first class view of the Float Line start-up.

As a team, the foremen and men began checking all conditions for start-up at about 6.00 a.m. to make sure we could start without any trouble at 9.00 a.m.

When I was satisfied about all conditions and temperatures were O.K. at 9.00 a.m. I gave the order and controlled all operations to allow the glass to flow from the furnace into the float bath.

The foremen and men had a hard hot struggle to row the hot glass through the float bath, but after about 25 minutes, we had glass on the lehr being pulled along nice and smoothly.

Afterwards there is always approximately two to three hours hot work to do, by sealing up the bath, setting up restrictor tiles, and many jobs around the furnace and annealing lehr under many times hot glass, atmospheric conditions, also the lifting and fitting into position the water coolers and also the cleaning up of tin oxide or dross.

Under all the circumstances, considering we had plenty of V.I.P.'s watching for the very first time, the men were a credit to the firm, but absolutely tired, and some of them had worked a double shift to help out.

It was about 12.00 noon when I was confident that everything was going according to plan, it was then when I flopped down exhausted and said I am going home. I had been in work from 5.00 a.m. and I had only gone home at midnight the previous night.

My Manager then said to me that there was a special V.I.P. lunch in the canteen and I had been invited and would I go along to it. I then replied that I was sick, tired and weary and that I would be satisfied to revert back as a normal workman, for at that time being staff the workmen were getting better overtime money than I was, also I was being under-paid for glassmaking knowledge, and ever increasing responsibilities, and like other men, my family and home life was being left at one side for glassmaking.

Anyway, instead of going to the canteen I went to the pub, had a couple of beers and then home to bed.

When my manager went along to the Lunch, Alastair Pilkington wanted to know why I had not come to the V.I.P. lunch. My manger quite rightly told him my opinion, and that I had gone home and I was too tired.

It was about 5.00 p.m. in the afternoon, my wife called me to say that my manager had come to our house to see me and he was waiting in the lounge. He then informed me that the Director had sent him to ask me if I would consider promotion and accept the managership of the new float line which I agreed to now that I had had, a good afternoon's sleep.

Next day when I went to work, the Works Manager sent for me and officially told me I was promoted to manager of C.H. 4 float line with a salary increase which I accepted.

Of course I realised this meant taking on a much wider range of responsibilities in excess of what I already had.

I was fortunate to be in a position that I had been in the forefront in practice and experimental work of everything, even plant, which included new designs, chemistry and all other new methods appertaining to the production of float glass.

This was a challenge I had to accept, knowing that outside glassmaking I did not have any schooling or trade qualifications to my name no matter how small, but I knew I had the backing of management, foremen and men because we were all one team working in the interest of float future.

It was in the Spring that P.P.G. sent over their production team to commence their four week training of the float process; at that time my position was Senior Foreman of the float lines.

I was give the job of looking after them, which included training in the classroom, practical training on the float lines, and the organising of entertainment for them outside working hours.

The problems of float glass manufacture had not been mastered at this time, and it was not possible to present anyone with a know-how manual in the making of float glass.

I would like to point out that Senior Management were very few and extremely busy with many things like administration changes, future designs, etc.

My manager had every confidence in myself and the foremen and wherever possible he gave me a free hand to train them the only way we knew how at the time, which was mostly practical training on site with their respective opposite numbers, foremen with foremen, men with men, I trained the manager and we all pulled together as one big team.

7

FLOAT TRAINING

It was most important that a good relationship between the P.P.G. production team and the Pilkington production team which was already chosen to go to America when the time came, was established as quickly as possible, to gain each others confidence and interest in the training programme. This we did by encouraging social entertainment.

Before entertainment outings I would have a discussion with my manager on where to take them. The times he did not go himself, he gave me the authority to draw as much money as I required to cover expenses on an I.O.U. slip, which was accounted for afterwards of which there were never any problems.

If working conditions permitted sometimes I would take both full teams. This happened twice, once to Chester and once to Blackpool.

In the coach it was noticeable that each sat with their opposite team mates and this encouraged a good working personnel friendship, by singing, joking and even discussing their respective jobs and families with one another.

Before we set off I would book in a restaurant for a specific number for dinner, and get a fixed price per head, plus a couple of drinks for everyone during dinner. This money I would put at one side, because there would be approx. 40 men.

I also gave each Pilkington man a couple of pounds to buy his opposite number a couple of drinks and I would inform them that after the meal, there was no restrictions on where they took the Americans, or what they did as long as they all behaved themselves and were back at the meeting point at the arranged time, no later, or we would go without them (there were no late ones).

The reason I did it this way was because (a) I was responsible for the whole party (b) I knew I had a great set of men who would not let me down, (c) the men had well earned a break of this kind, and (d) I was convinced this was the correct way to establish a good trusting social relationship which was so important to Pilkington's, because at this time the eyes of the glass world were on us and mainly how could anyone hope to control 30-40 men at Blackpool and Chester unless it was done this way.

During the 4 weeks training period a lot of overtime and hard sweating work was a necessity because:

(a)   Everytime there was any shut down, or calamity, or work in progress on any float line the Americans had to be there even if they were in bed at the Fleece Hotel, where they were staying, we would call them in.

(b)   We built a small bath and kiln, and in training, we did our best to reproduce and demonstrate the dangers of tin leak and emergency procedures.

It must still be remembered all was practical men's work, and it was the duty and job of the men to impress the Americans that the float process was a practical working success. Because this is what the glass world was looking for.

The American team were really amazed at the technical knowledge our glassmaking foremen and workmen had gained, considering, they were only unskilled men, with no academical qualifications for nearly everyone in their team was holding some High School qualification or other. It was unbelieveable to them.

The P.P.G. team were finding float glass work very hot and thirsty, but not to worry, our boys had all the answers to keep them interested and happy. Some of them took the Americans to the pub, the clubs and even to their homes to meet the wives and families. If I am not mistaken, everyone went to someone's home or social functions with them sometime or other, as I used to take them to my home. This was another great contribution to float success, which was needed to relieve pressure from senior management by the workmen.

On a couple of occasions we had a social night with the Americans in City Road Club, a few drinks and sandwiches, in which case any float glass line worker who came along was included in free drinks and sandwiches, for this was a little perk I fully believed they deserved, and believe me it was well appreciated by the men. Luckily for me paying the bill, then management never once questioned how much I spent on them, for it was worth it to Pilkington's at the time to keep a good happy working relationship with our men and the first licensee team; but the workmen really did put themselves out even at the expenses of their home and family commitments many-a-time.

It was noticeable at this time that not only were the eyes of the glass world on our men, but a lot of eyes in the Pilkington works were on them as well, saying what a good time these chaps are having, but we knew it was only a temporary perk or two to get the show on the road as the Americans say.

By now signs were showing of empire building taking place in administration departments, personnel, training, safety first, engineering, new intakes of young development workers, 'O' Levels, 'A' Levels, BSc's, PhD's all being trained to be the future heads and management of the float lines and works departments.

The men understood the new policies which were being formed, but it was a pity some of the senior people were not really down to earth, for there was one especially — and possibly another — of the senior foremen who had given their everything for the success of float, who were absolutely brilliant and would have made excellent managers, for what the firm required from them.

Although we had began licensing and training of licensees we were still in the float development stage, because we hadn't mastered the ways successfully of making thinner glass than 6.5 mm. Also, we hadn't even tried to make thicker glasses, and we were still having many problems with the bath chemistry, which was creating top tin speck occasionally.

We were having problems with distortion for good quality glass and it was these kind of problems that the foremen and men were working hard on using every scrap of practical experience they could muster up between them, because we knew so much research and development theories had been put forward, some working, some not, that there must be some

51

practical answers, somewhere only practical glassmakers could put forward and operate.

Many a time when things went wrong the only people who would be there at the time were the foremen and men, and occasionally one or the other would notice a temporary change of condition of some kind, and would make a suggestion as to how to prevent the same thing happening again which was noted as valuable information.

It was through these channels of information that a lot of answers to ribbon control and bath cleanliness as to tin oxide, was slowly but surely gained.

With constant observation by the Foremen and workmen, we were able to set new parameters for many things like temperatures, speeds of draw and very important, tin deposits on lehr rollers, as which roller was affecting the glass and marking it.

It must be said that the examiners at the lehr end were unskilled men belonging to the float line department, and there was an excellent relationship and co-operation between the foremen at the float line, and the examination foreman which was proved to be very valuable and many a fault was spotted and analysed between them as to where the fault originated from.

Although the float line workers were members of General and Municipal Workers Union the Union top men kept a very low profile, and never intervened about working conditions, overtime, pay rates or promotion during the early stages of Float, which was a big asset to the float glass development process at this time.

The scheduled date for the P.P.G. new float line start-up was November 18th 1963 at Cumberland, Maryland, U.S.A.

A start-up team was picked from the float glass people of 2 Managers, 1 Senior Foreman, 3 Shift Foremen and 12 Workmen Operators.

This was the beginning of a new era of ambassadors preparing to change the whole flat glass industry throughout the world, from plate and sheet glass manufacture to float glass manufacture.

Because of the training of the P.P.G. team and the C.H.4 float line conversion, many of the men held back on having their holidays, as they felt that they did not want to jeopardize the float process at this critical stage. Of course this not only affected the job and workmen, but the families, wives and children were beginning to tire of all work and no recreation, or rest holidays.

Yes, the summer of 1963 was a very hard one. On No. 1 float line we were in a heavy development programme of making thin glass by edge roll machines, which needed extra men. No. 3 line was making 6.5 mm glass still having occasional teething problems, No. 4 line was in its infancy, full of teething problems, and it was a matter of foremen and men helping each other out by staying on and working overtime practically every other day.

Most of the problems I am now referring to at this period were:

(a) The chemistry of the bath had not been mastered and there was a lot of tin oxide being made, forming dross, which affected quality.

(b) Distortion was still giving problems and many equipment changes were constantly being re-adjusted.

(c) Substance variations across the ribbon width were not always as required.

(d) Ribbon stabilization sometimes erratic.

(e) Exit end breaks, owing to temperatures being too cold.

(f) Many of the men were still in the learning stages.

(g) When there was any trouble in the bath, it was very important that everyone in the team knew exactly what he had to do, and how to do it, otherwise one man could prolong the rowing session, or do even more serious damage to the line, such as damaging the lift out rollers.

There is no doubt that a float line costs millions of pounds, and for many hours every day, e.g. during the night, Bank Holidays, week-ends, the only people working on the lines, controlling the lines, and actually taking the responsibility at the times stated, for plant safety, security and glassmaking were the shift foremen and workmen.

I cannot emphasise this point enough, because at this time there was no closed circuit television cameras, no early warning systems to warn, before things actually got out of control, as at the standards of today. It was a matter of everyone being alert, watching, working and praying nothing would go wrong, and it was because of this dedication to job that many good ideas were put forward by the men, which contributed to float glass efficiency.

Lunchtime at Sheet Works.

Acknowledgement St. Helens Local History and Archives Library.

8

AMERICAN TRIPS

When the time came for the first start-up team to go out to
P.P.G., it was agreed the team would go out late November. I
was scheduled to go, but the date was brought forward to the
16th November and as my daughter was getting married on the
18th November, in no way could I go to America, which was
understandable.

In the actual start-up team there were two managers (one for
glass making and one for chemistry) one senior foreman, 4 shift
foremen and 12 workmen.

For some of the men it was the first time they had been away
from home, and they were very anxious that they would get back
home in time for Christmas. Because of past experiences on
start-up time to saleable glass on a new line, especially a foreign
one, it could be anyone's guess how long it would take.

The team was kitted out, cases, clothes, allowances, and they
took their own safety clothing and asbestos mitts.

On the way out they were allowed a stay in New York, and
when they got to P.P.G. float line in Cumberland, they were
given eight dollars a day to cover food allowances and spend.

The men worked hard with lots of overtime on this P.P.G. first
start-up.

They had built up a good working relationship with their
opposite working partners while they were in England which
helped both sides to get away to a reasonably good start-up,

which was early December.

With it being Christmas, the full team came home two days before Christmas day, with the P.P.G. people hoping to make good saleable float glass after the Christmas holidays.

It was arranged that I would go out on December 28 1963 to continue helping them with their float glass manufacturing problems, and stay for a period of six weeks. This I did.

On 20th December 1963, my manager asked me if I was prepared to go to help and advise them in the manufacture of float glass on their new float glass line. This I agreed to, and I must confess I was looking forward to going to American and also going in an aeroplane for the first time. Yes, it was going to be a big thrill for me; at that time I was over the moon as the saying goes.

When I went home and told my wife I was going to America on December 28th the conversation went into a serious question time, e.g. Why couldn't it wait until the New Year? Why are you going on your own? Are you confident you can cope with all their problems? Will you be alright flying?

Then there were the extra shopping problems of Christmas time, buying and preparing extra clothes. I was happy but when I look back, it was a very hard confusing time for my wife. I am sure we are all aware of how much extra effort is put into the preparation for the Christmas festivities by all wives and mothers to keep families happy and well fed.

The 28th December was a cold wet day, I went to Liverpool airport to catch a plane to London, and it was only when I was kissing my wife just before going to the departure gates that I realised how much she had given up over the Christmas holiday, and how much she was going to miss me over the next six weeks and how much we loved each other. A big lump came in my throat which prevented me from saying "Goodbye love". I walked away with tears in my eyes.

On the flight down to London I was a little scared with it being my first time and I must confess it was a great relief to put my feet on the ground again. The flying time was 50 minutes and during those 50 minutes it went through my mind about the flight to America and how I could face up to the long air journey, believe me, at the time I wasn't looking forward to it.

When I arrived in London it was 8.00pm and as the flight to America was 8.00am the 29th from Heathrow, Pilkington's had booked me a room at the Aerial Hotel next to the airport for the night. My first job was to phone my wife and say I had arrived in London.

It was a relief to be able to say everything I wanted to say, for by now the lump had gone out of my throat as we both understood our love and feelings for each other, and our children.

A coach collected me at the Aerial Hotel at 6.00am for the 8.00am flight to New York.

As I was sitting in the departure lounge, all sorts of possibilities for plane disasters went through my mind and what would happen to my family, which I loved so much. I even went to the insurance desk and bought extra insurance, for which my wife received the receipt a week later. Oh yes, I was afraid at that time.

While waiting in the departure lounge I had my eyes fixed on some of the planes I could see outside and I was shaking and wondering which plane would take me to America. I was praying it would be the large one I could see furthest away from the terminal gate, which we were driven to. It was a Boeing 707 BOAC. As I walked up the steps of the plane I was amazed at the size of it, for there was a vast difference between the 707 and the small one I had flown in the night before from Liverpool. As I took my seat on the plane I felt a sense of greater security on a larger plane, this took away some of my fear.

With having a window seat and it being a day time flight, and the plane being only half full, as the time crept on, I could feel myself forgetting about the dangers of flying and I was beginning to enjoy it to the extent that after about four hours I took my shoes off, put my slippers on and ordered a drink. Yes, it was good and refreshing, so I ordered another and as I sat staring through the aircraft window looking down on the snow capped hills and open spaces of Newfoundland and Canada, it came into my mind: "By jove, this is better than working, I like it." From then onwards my fear of flying completely vanished. Oh what a lovely flight it was, nice, quiet and steady, all the way to New York.

At New York I had to transfer to a T.W.A. flight to Washington, that was approximately 1½ hours flying time.

From Dulles Airport in Washington, I was driven by bus to the Hilton Hotel in Pittsburgh, where I stayed the night.

After a good night's sleep I woke up about 7.30am and I looked through the window and I could see it was very cold outside, everywhere was covered with ice and snow.

When I went down to breakfast at 8.30am I was all set in my mind to order a good hot English breakfast of eggs, bacon and a pot of hot tea.

I sat at a table, and the first item I noticed was a glass of ice water on the table, I asked the waitress for a cup of tea and she returned with a glass of tea with ice in it. I smiled and said: "Please, I want hot tea." There was a gentleman on the next table who heard our conversation about the tea and he said to me: "Excuse me please, but why don't you try it as we like it, the American way". I said: "What way is that"?

He replied, "First of all we scald the tea, next we pour it over ice to cool it down then we put lemon in to flavour it and afterwards put sugar in to sweeten it." This was my first impression of the crazy American cup of tea.

I tried it, but I did not like the American way of brewing tea, so I drank coffee which is their national drink. The breakfast being served at the time was a continental breakfast, which was bread rolls with butter and little pots of different marmalades which I enjoyed.

It was on the morning of December 30th that I was driven to the factory, the weather was cold and everything seemed so cold and dismal.

The first reaction by the works' manager was: "We are not making good glass, come and have a look and tell us why."

Now I realised several points which had not occurred to me before.

(a)   I was completely on my own in another country.
(b)   I was the first float glass maker to go out trouble shooting.
(c)   My orders from Pilkingtons were as follows:
(d)   This is our first Licensee, do not do any work, or interfere with any other section of the float line only the bath section, as that is the only section they have licensed from us, which means the tank and the lehr is their responsibility.
(e)   Yes, they all respected me, but as Tommy Grundy, the senior foreman, whom they knew me as when we last met, when training in England. I with no academical schooling qualifications to my name.

I could see straight away what a tough job I had facing me, manually and politically, but I reassured myself that I had come to help them, and teach them about float glass, and not them to teach and hinder me, at the expense of the good name of Pilkingtons, or myself.

When I got to the line, I had a good look around the float bath and was satisfied as to what I saw, that our boys had done their job well, during and after the start-up period.

From the float bath side, there was only one thing stopping them from making saleable glass, and that was, at the end of the bath there was dross and pieces of cullet under the ribbon, these were causing scratches on the bottom surface of the glass.

I pointed this problem out to their line manager, and asked him to clean out the dross and cullet, his reply was that he would sooner me do it, as it was a dangerous job for his inexperienced men, so I did the job myself, without any problem, which ultimately removed the scratches on the glass.

During the course of our conversation, I was told that they were having problems with road transport, due to bad conditions with ice and snow, which meant that hydrogen and nitrogen, required for the float bath, was down to the absolute minimum, and over the Christmas period they had been reluctant to open the bath to do anything until I came. This I understood and agreed with.

My time at P.P.G. was not easy, for I was confronted with many technical and political problems and questions.

They were having many glass making problems and I knew they were not the float bath problems as we knew them.

I had been there about two weeks and I was getting really fed up about my hands being tied, because although I was not supposed to look at anything, I decided to have a look into their annealing lehr.

It was Sunday morning about 9 a.m. when I knew no one would be watching me, I decided to really go to town and have a good survey of the lehr.

First of all what was happening, the float glass was coming out of the bath at normal temperature conditions 600°C, and then instead of the glass cooling down and being annealed as we did, and they knew how we did it in England, they were doing it entirely different.

When P.P.G. and Pilkington management had telephone conversations about the progress, and process, the P.P.G. people knew the timing of each phone call and made it inconvenient for me to be there in the office at that time, for they would always tell me afterwards.

My findings about the lehr were reported to Pilkington's and I asked for a survey to be done on glass temperature in our Lehr at Cowley Hill No. 3.

This was done, and the temperatures were phoned out to me by arrangement.

P.P.G. were reluctant to cool down the lehr, but ultimately they had to cool down the lehr to similar temperatures as at Cowley Hill.

Although the lehr rollers were cooled down to Cowley Hill temperatures, the damage to the lehr rollers had been done by being too hot and they had to be cleaned before good saleable glass could be produced.

Cumberland was in Maryland, a small town on the border line with West Virginia, and a couple of miles from the Mason Dixon Line, and at the foothills of the Allagheny Mountains.

It seemed to be a small mixed community of different breeds, for example, a part of the Township was for Cherokee Indians, and just like some of our towns, there were West Virginians and different nationals, Italians, etc. but with it being such a small town, it was more noticeable.

There wasn't much to do out of working hours, for it was Winter time, the roads were icy and snow bound for most of the time I was there; and it was a matter of going to work everyday, then returning to the Cumberland Hotel, which was about the only one in town open at this time, the bar conversation was about rattlesnakes and the Civil War.

I remember it quite well, it had a long bar, and the first night I went into it the barman said, be careful, watch those holes in the bar, I replied which holes, and he said, the ones the British boys made with their elbows. I think I made them a little deeper.

The factory itself was a few miles away in what seemed to be a bleak isolated country spot. They had no canteen as we have in our factory, and at lunch time it was a matter of being driven out to old Joe's roadside cafe for maybe soup or a bun and coffee — probably a beautiful country place in the Summer.

This was their way of life in Cumberland which was accepted by us as I realised by talking with the men afterwards.

At the end of my six weeks I returned home, and reported on many points I had noted while I was there, and discussions which had taken place between myself and the P.P.G. float team.

It was in May 1964 when the next set of licencees came over for training, they were the L.O.F. team from Lathrop in

California USA.

By now the Foreman and workmen were a little more advanced in the practical methods of training with their respective numbers, but it was still very important to Pilkingtons that our men did their jobs right and acted as good ambassadors which they did exceptionally well, also there was still plenty of hard work on our own float lines because we had not mastered the thin glass problem, and thicker glasses we had not started on.

A similar start up team was picked to go out to California, but this time there was a change, to give some other Foremen and men licensing experiences.

It was the beginning of August when the start up team left England. They flew out to California without an overnight stay, and the day they got there it was 90°F, nice and hot.

Once again, the Foremen and men were put on shifts, and the preparation work began, but under severe heat conditions we had never experienced.

California was a different place altogether than Maryland. The weather was exceptionally hot, it was summertime, the factory was situated in a farming area known as Lathrop, approximately 20 miles from San Francisco, and three miles from Stockton.

L.O.F. had built a big new greenfield Factory at Lathrop for float glass production, and it was built on a bit of desert land surrounded by beautiful scenery, because at that time of the year, the fields were full of grapes, peaches, tomatoes, oranges, apples, nuts ready on the trees, always a beautiful blue sky, no rain, all the 12 weeks we were there. Plenty of ice cold beer — sounds like heaven except for the hard work we all had to do.

One of the hard parts about something like I have just quoted, and the men used to say it many a time, was, if only our wives and families could be here to see all this. I would give anything for them to be here now, or even at home with them.

Because of shift work, and most of the L.O.F. foremen and men living in a small village named Manteca, which was about one-and-a-half miles from the factory, our foremen and men were living in a Motel in Manteca. The name of the Motel was the Starlight which had everything they required, good beds, good food, bar, and a swimming pool of their own.

Everyone, sometime or other, had visits to San Francisco, Lake Tahoe, Yosemite National Park where the Redwood Trees are, for the Californians were very appreciative of the hard sweating

61

work of our men were doing, also the L.O.F. team remembered the good social relationship our men helped them to enjoy when they were in St Helens.

One highlight which happened:

Early one morning we were called in because the float line had shut down. What had happened, the electricity generator was in the field near the factory, with just a wire fencing around it. Someone was chasing a fox, and the fox jumped through the wire fence into the live cables, killing the fox and putting the generator out of action. This resulted in loss of electricity to the factory, and gave us a good day's hard work cleaning up the float bath, and then starting up again (this could only happen in California).

During daytime hours, as the hot work was in progress, because of the hot climate we only progressed with some of the hot jobs, at half the speed we normally did, e.g. when fitting restrictor tiles in the bath or changing a tweel in the canal and making up, or sealing up.

After a few minutes we had to go outside in the shade, have a drink, and rest, but everyone of the team really pulled out everything, and every ounce of energy they had to start up on the given day, our men really impressed the Americans.

Although this was the second licensee start up there were still many points we did not know about the chemistry and reaction of refractories, and molten tin as to glass making.

When we started up, the ribbon was just one mass of big bubbles, each about the size of a marble. This was something we hadn't experienced before on such a large scale, it was really baffling us, but this type of catastrophe created lots of hard sweating work for the foremen and men, really it was disheartening at the time.

It was a very serious mishap and after a few days of trying everything we knew, Alastair Pilkington and a couple of Technical Managers came out.

After long discussions it was decided to shut the float bath down and make one or two modifications at the exit end of the bath and then put in some more tin to give a deeper tin depth.

To do this some tin had to be drained out of the bath while the bath was hot.

It was most unfortunate that one of our men got a flash back as he opened up one of the sections, and got his face burned and had to go home to England for treatment.

62

Also, while we were in the process of draining the tin out of the bath, an air compressor in a building at the side of the bath we were working on, blew up. This shook everyone of us up for a few hours, but luckily, apart from being shaken up, everyone was O.K.

We started up again three days later, but this time without the big bubbles, but it was still hot, heavy and hard for foremen and men, because of the extreme heat, but they never gave up.

The L.O.F. Vice President, who was the one who was really down to earth, quoted many a time, I don't know what we would have done without the hard work and sheer guts and faith in their jobs of the British Boys.

This was a 12 week job away from home, once again the wives, families and children were still waiting patiently for their return.

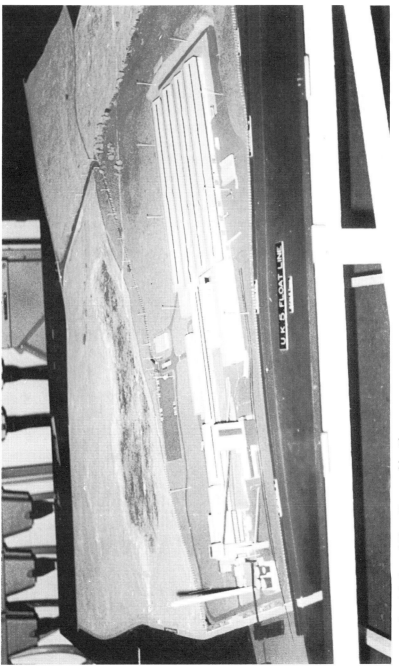

A typical aerial view of Float Line world wide.

9

RONALD REAGAN

Air Products had built a small chemical factory, a few yards outside the boundary line of the Float Glass Factory at Lathrop California, purposely for the manufacture of Nitrogen and Hydrogen for the float bath.

When the float line began production of saleable float glass, a huge marquee was erected inside the Air Products factory and it was made known to us that, the Governor of California, Ronald Reagan (who later became President of the USA) was being invited to officially open the Air Products Factory but he would not be allowed to see the Float Process, as it was under licence secrecy.

At the opening ceremony we were invited to go to the marquee for 1.45 p.m. for drinks before the opening at 2.00 p.m. on the opening day.

We had all been working hard in very hot conditions and at 1.00 p.m. we stopped work and began cleaning ourselves up, first taking off our dirty sweaty clothes, having a shower or bath then putting on clean shirts and shorts. Admittedly we were not in our Sunday best clothes but we all looked good clean respectable English workmen as we walked across to the marquee ready for the reception.

Some of us had never heard of Ronald Reagan although he was an actor and Governor of California.

When we arrived inside the marquee the Air Products director greeted us with what he called Southern Comfort style, which happened to be a glass of Southern Comfort whisky and ice, this he said would give us encouragement to mix and enjoy the happy occasion.

Of course the Vice President of Libbey-Owens-Ford, Henry Dodge, who this time was our greatest ally, had arranged for this special drink for he was a great whisky drinker himself, so he appreciated it if our boys just called him Hank, for he loved to be known as Hank Dodge, and not Henry or Sir.

Naturally we kept in our little group, and as we looked around the marquee it was quite noticeable to us that many of different types of high ranking American celebrities had been invited to the opening ceremony, all standing around in their own little groups drinking, chatting away, all enjoying themselves ever so casual and welcoming.

At 2.00 p.m. the Air Products Director called for order and requested that everyone be seated, for the official opening of the Air Products factory by the Governor of California Ronald Reagan.

I must confess up to that day I had never heard of him or seen a photograph of him, because just like most of the other boys, our priorities had always been at Pilkingtons.

We were asked to sit on the front row which made us feel like VIPs.

Ronald Reagan came to the front of the marquee and stood facing us all.

He stood perfectly upright, dressed very smart in his suit and tie, sporting a good athletic figure, with a smile on his face, the smile that puts everyone at ease.

His first words were to welcome the British Boys to California.

Next he spoke of the Air Products organisation and why they had built this chemical plant in Lathrop Califoronia. Then in a very diplomatic way, he smiled and said, I cannot speak about the new glass making process, because I know nothing about it, as it is under strict licensing agreements, of which I am sure is going to be a world winner, at the same time, once again here we have a good example of Anglo-American industrial relationship, I know will grow and prosper in the coming years.

After the little speech there was a conducted tour of the Air Products factory which was led by the Director and Ronald Reagan, this lasted for approximately 20 minutes.

Yes by now we knew who Ronald Reagan was, and as we

walked around, I am sure our main interest at the time was admiring the ease and confidence of this man, and even now and again he would converse with different people, even to the extent of making a little remark to make people smile.

After the conducted tour we all returned to the marquee for a buffet lunch and drinks.

As we were all stood around in our own little groups waiting, drinking and talking which is normal on these occasions, Hank Dodge the Vice President of Libbey Owens Ford who was with out group said "Hey! you guys, here is the Governor coming to shake your hands".

He came over to us with a glass of wine in his hand, in such a casual American way, that made us feel at ease to the effect that when he asked us how did we enjoy the Californian weather one of the boys replied, "It goes down well with this ice cold beer Sir", and as Ronald Reagan was laughing at the remark, Hank Dodge spoke up to him and said, "here are some of the guys that made this project possible".

Ronald Reagan shook hands with each one of us and wished us all a happy stay in California and every success in our new glassmaking travels and then he moved on to another group.

First European start-up at Glaverbel, Belgium.

10

EUROPE

Our next licensee was Glaverbel from Moustier in Belgium, This one was a real tough one, because of language difficulties.

Two Americans, P.P.G. and L.O.F., were helped because everyone spoke the same language, they also had more academicals in their teams.

It has often been said the English people are very lazy as to learning foreign languages, in comparison as to foreigners learning English. I found it true.

When the licencees for Glaverbel came to actually talk about the float glass making, it was in June 1964, three of their managers had a discussion with us, about a training programme for the Glaverbel start up team, and right from the beginning of glassmaking discussions it was noticable that we were relying on the Belgian management to do the translation, for they would speak English more fluently than anyone from our management could speak French.

During the discussions, it was decided that one of our Senior Foremen and myself would go to Belgium in July and spend two weeks at their factory at Moustier.

When we got there we found that the Belgian glassmakers were similar to our men, except they spoke a different language.

Our first job was to get them in the classroom and talk to them through their manager, who were the interpreters for us, all the advantages of changing from plate glass to float glass.

Bluntly, we had to sell float to the Glaverbel glassmakers who were Shop Floor workmen, for 80% of their team were these people.

When we had gained their confidence the serious training began, and each day with various models we had made by the Belgians, we demonstrated as best we could, on how a float bath operated, and as practically as possible, we put over the chemistry, the atmosphere gases, the electrical heating, the hot-tin, the bath superstructure and the full outline of how a float bath operated.

We also had to point out the dangers of mistakes, also about the cost to plant and most important, personnel safety.

After the first eight days when we had gone and done much talking and demonstrations by model work, we had two full days of open discussions and questions, and we realised the team had been paying a lot of attention to what we had been teaching them in preparation for coming to St Helens.

Many of the team had never been out of their own districts, and were very concerned as to what it would be like over in St Helens. Here again, we went through a kind of social expectancy training period, for just like out men they also had families who were interested in what they would be doing, and how long they would be away from home, and the working life, and social life they would encounter in St Helens.

It was October 1964 the Glaverbel team came for their four weeks training period at Cowley Hill Works. The team comprised of three Managers, all three could speak English fluently, four Foremen, one could speak English and 16 workmen, 14 speaking no English.

At this stage we did have an interpreter from our Head Office brought in to the training programme but he did not fully understand the float process. However, he was a massive help to us during the training period at Cowley Hill Works.

In the Pilkington start-up team we picked to work with and train the Glaverbel team, was again a slightly different set of men than previous because it was our policy at this period to encourage and train as many as possible for future licensing commitments which was now showing signs of becoming heavier in future years.

Glaverbel was the first European glass manufacturer to obtain a float glass licence and it was quite obvious that the eyes of our European competitors, Boussois, Saint Gobain and others were watching with interest how this new technical process was being handled and worked successfully by the practical men, which put our glassmakers once again in the front line for hard work, and the politics of float glass manufacture, because if they failed to do a good job then it would do harm to float confidence in Europe.

When the Glaverbel team came to Cowley Hill it was decided to keep them all on days for the first week.

The reason being most of them could not speak English so they had daily talks in the classroom, and occasionally had training on the float bath mixing as much as possible with their opposite numbers, even to the effect of social entertainment at lunch times and evenings so they could all get to know each other and gain each other's confidence before they commenced shift work.

Our boys responded magnificently and even took them to their homes to meet their families and children which helped to promote a teaching relationship which would have taken years to obtain any other way.

The foremen and men of the Pilkington float lines had to teach these licensees faster than any college and also take the responsibility for their immediate results when put into practice.

It proved this in America, because when the lines started up our foremen and workmen were on shift work with the Americans who could speak English, but during night-time and weekends if any problems arose it was the Pilkington men who had to take the responsibility at the immediate time, and put it right, which was an added responsibility; they were also there to see the licensee shift workers didn't make mistakes.

A mistake in a classroom can be more easily rectified than a mistake on a float bath which could result in loss of plant, glass or serious injury to personnel.

After the first week of training at Cowley Hill the Glaverbel foremen and men were put on shift work. The reason for this was to ensure that no matter what type of working conditions or problems we had to face on a float line someone would always be there to see and learn about our methods of operating it.

If any emergency arose, or any special job was going to take place, then the managers and full Glaverbel team if possible would be called in to see.

Sometimes, as the men used to say, it can become entertaining teaching someone your job, and at other times it can become a bore and tiring, especially when it is hard to make the person understand because of language problems.

As one man put it: I don't know what I will do if we have any problems and have to row the glass through the float bath for my arms are falling off now, explaining to these foreigners about the job. They don't understand English and so they talk with their hands and arms and they have us doing the same. But no problem, we can both lift up a pint glass and have a laugh afterwards, we will teach them alright.

For this period of training our Pilkington interpreter had a list typed out for each man in both teams, spelling and explaining the French and English necessities around a float bath which helped the English learn bits of French — that was very helpful. It was the same with the Belgians and it was amazing how quickly an understanding relationship of the workings of the float process and social points developed. This was the beginning of another asset to float licensing by the foremen and workmen.

The Glaverbel start-up at Moustier in Belgium was due in March 1965. The Pilkington team went out to the Glaverbel factory at Moustier in February 1965, two weeks prior to start-up.

They stayed at a small hotel in Namur which is about 50 miles from Brussels and travelled by car each day to Moustier which was approximately two miles away.

Namur was an average size town, and in summer time it is an attractive tourist spot. It has a castle, and also a beautiful view of the valley where the river Meuse and three other rivers meet. It has a decent size shopping centre set out for the tourist trade with many small bars, but it was winter time when the team stayed there, which was dull, dark and dismal, especially at night-time.

Moustier is a small industrial village with no hotel large enough to accommodate the Pilkington team.

The factory was old and had two small plate glass furnaces working at the time. I don't think there was a canteen, I never saw one, and it was a matter of our men being issued with packed lunches for meals at work, with either coffee or beer; also there was a small locker room with two showers, but the Pilkington team were now having to accept a new working environment which was well below the standards they had been used to back home (as they say, there is no place like home).

Apparently the small hotel where the men stayed at in Namur was well below the standards of the average British hotel. It served drinks 24 hours a day, with a noisy juke box banging away most of the night and day and it created a real nuisance to the men's sleep, especially when the men had been working on night shift.

A change of food tastes due to the different ways of cooking and flavouring was encountered.

The different exchange rates and prices for goods were soon overcome by the men.

Language problems were eased a lot because in Belgium the common language is mostly French and also it is amazing how many people, especially hoteliers and shop owners have taught themselves enough English to enable them to converse. Perhaps with Namur being a summer tourist town this is understandable.

When a team of Englishmen are away from home for a long period of 12 weeks in these circumstances it is important that their off-duty social life is catered for.

The Belgian people of Namur and Moustier got to know them, accepted them and most of all respected them, for their hard work, loyalty to the job and people. We never had any complaint of any description from anyone on either side. As a matter of fact they were good ambassadors for English behaviour as well as for Pilkingtons. I am not saying they were angels, but responsible workers, away from home in a new environment.

The Glaverbel management were anxious that we gave them a little more help with preparatory work than we had anticipated.

They were behind schedule with their furnace jobs, so this meant more hot work and responsibility for our men, so the Pilkington foremen and the other men started on shift work immediately.

This time it was like doing another training programme. Because of language difficulties, the training that we gave them in St Helens hadn't really got home to all of the Glaverbel team to enable them to put training into practice. This was understandable, because although they were hard workers and intelligent, experience was not on their side, nor were educational standards.

I remember the morning we started glassmaking, our foremen

73

and men worked double shifts, we started up at 9.00am and went through the normal routine of sealing up the bath and from the Pilkington side everything was going well and the men were being congratulated on a good start up.

In the afternoon the Glaverbel furnace men were setting up the canal section where the glass flows through from the furnace to the float bath; by accident, one of them let a metal radiation pyrometer fall into the glass at the point where the glass depth was 39″, this was the beginning of a very difficult start up period.

The metal radiation pyrometer created a tremendous amount of bubble in the glass and the first priority was to find the metal pyrometer and remove it from the canal section.

As the Glaverbel workmen fished about in the canal trying to locate the metal pyrometer, this automatically played havoc with glass control and temperature requirements required for steady glassmaking conditions in the float bath. This went on for two days without any success. During this period, the Pilkington team had to work very hard and use every bit of knowledge and experience gained from years when we used to shut down every week with lots of unknown problems.

After two days failure to locate the metal pyrometer in the canal, a team of furnace experts came from Holland. These people had been trained for this type of work.

The Dutch team fished around for another couple of days before locating the metal pyrometer at the bottom of the canal and successfully removing it from the glass in the canal.

This operation again played havoc with the float bath conditions and because of drastic temperature changes, over which we had no control, the glass at the exit end of the bath was periodically breaking.

By this time the Pilkington workmen were absolutely shattered with the continuous hard work, with plenty of overtime, rowing the glass through the hot float bath, which was now in a very bad condition, with bits of broken glass and plenty of tin dross floating around, plus the fact that the Pilkington men were more or less taking the responsibility for the practical efforts, and training of the Glaverbel men, under conditions the Glaverbel men never dreamed of; it was forced upon us to shut down for a few hours to clean the bath out ready for a cleaner start-up.

As one of the Glaverbel managers remarked to me after we started up again, the Pilkington foremen and men were real workaholics and happy and humorous with it, for they had team spirit. When everything seemed lost someone would come out with a refreshing joke, or burst into song. What else could they do? They had a responsible job to do for Pilkingtons, away from home, and they did it well without complaint. Yes this was the spirit which was one of the cushions in the early days of float success.

The morale of the Glaverbel team was a little low, with the unexpected disasters and hard work they were experiencing at this time in this new glassmaking environment. It was noticed that they had a couple of workmen who could sing, and smile, and crack jokes when all was going wrong and at the same time do their job well and set good examples. These same men moulded in very well with our own men even outside of work and helped them to enjoy life by taking them to their homes and showing them around various areas.

After about four weeks hard work, Glaverbel did start producing saleable glass, but the supervision and training of the Glaverbel foremen and men by our foremen and men was still carrying on as they were on shift work; and really in many instances taking responsibility for the float bath operation.

The Glaverbel team began to gain confidence after about seven or eight weeks and started to show that they were ready to be left alone to do the job themselves.

This was good for Pilkington men but one or two little problems had still to be ironed out as they say, like the bath sealing, cleaning of rollers, etc.

The Pilkington team left after 12 weeks with compliments from all at Glaverbel; thus enhancing the name of Pilkington throughout Belgium and the rest of Europe.

It was noticeable, especially by the wives and some families of the men that being away 12 weeks doing a lot of hard work, and in new types of environment, with plenty of responsibilities, that some of them were really tired and needed a good rest away from work for a short while to recuperate. Also this applied to the wives and families who had sacrificed their love and care for 12 weeks during winter periods so the answer was many applied for holidays which were granted.

While the men were away in Belgium; the foremen and men back at St Helens were still working very hard and having to work overtime as the job required, because there were still many problems being encountered in the production and development of thinner glasses being made by the float process.

When I returned from Belgium I had been back three weeks when the works manager transferred me from my past position of Line Manager on No. 4, to the position of Line Manager No. 3, which was our biggest line, and also destined for future float development projects as well as continuous production.

During 1965 there were periods of excessive overtime, and extra responsibilities for the foremen and men of the float lines because we had sold licences to two Japanese glass manufacturers, Nippon and Asahi; also, to the West German manufacturing firm of San Roch who were at that time partners with Saint Gobain, also the French glass manufacturing firm of Boussois.

By now the firm had brought into the float lines more academicals being trained as managers and assistant managers also workmen from other departments like the grinding and polishing departments, which in numbers was very good but even at this stage many of them were still in the learning period.

All this really meant that in 1965 at various intervals we had the Nippon team for training, Asahi team for training, French team for training and the West German team for training and a team just back from Belgium in April. All this may sound unbelievable but it was true.

This was a very hard strenuous task for everyone working with the Float Process for example Licensing Dept., Engineering Dept., Development Dept., all Float Production Managers, Assistant Managers, Foremen and Workmen, especially as many of them were being, as it were, tried, trained and passed out in a hurry, hoping for success, which thank God most of them achieved and was noted.

I could not leave out this appreciation of others, but I specifically said this book was to highlight the contribution of the shop floor glass workers to the success of the float process. This I will now concentrate on.

Before a licensee team comes for training it is normal to pick which senior foreman, foremen and workmen are going to, for example, West Germany. So that the men can make arrangements with anything appertaining to their home life and to prepare themselves to be able to assist in the practical training of their opposite number in the licensee team, some even bought little dictionaries and sentence translations books to help them with the German language, and the money exchange from Sterling to Marks.

The German team that came over comprised of one manager, one senior foreman, four shift foremen and 16 workmen. Out of a team of 22 it was found that 10 of them could speak English which made matters and training easier for our foremen and men as far as translations were concerned.

The team from Pilkington was again changed from previous teams to the effect some of the foremen and workmen hadn't been abroad before and even a few of them had been promoted temporarily to jobs a little higher than their normal job for this purpose because of all the commitments that had to be filled at home and overseas in such a short time.

Everyone seemed to mould in well with the similar type of training programme I have mentioned previously; also the adaption of entertainment and social life. The men took the German counterparts to their homes and clubs, and they were accepted by the families because the wives and families did it in respect of their loved ones and the success of Float and Pilkington!

The German team stayed for four weeks and a few weeks later, four German managers came over for two weeks training from Saint Gobain.

Our team went out to Porz in Germany in early February 1966. Porz is a small town on the Rhine about eight miles from Cologne.

The factory was a medium size one producing approximately 1,500 tons of plate glass per week, and they built a float line in the same factory to produce approximately 2,000 tons of float glass per week.

Germany is noted for the carnival time which begins three days before the first day in Lent.

Our team got to Porz two days before carnival and on the first day of carnival the Saint Gobain management acknowledged what hospitality and help our men had given their men when training in St Helens by giving us all two days holiday so we could join in the celebrations.

On the first day there was a carnival parade through the centre of Cologne which lasted about two hours with bands, bunting, dancers, everything it takes to make a big parade. In the centre of Cologne there was a special grandstand viewing area with seats for mostly V.I.P.'s, and we were amazed to find some of the seats had been booked and reserved for the Pilkington men.

This the men really appreciated and it was the start of a good

77

working relationship between the German workers and our men in Germany.

By this time our foremen and men had gained a lot more experience of float bath hazards during start-up time; also the German team had the pick of the best men from some of the Saint Gobain factories, and successfully moulded them together into a good conscientious hard working team, which eventually eased a lot of hard work and responsibility off our foremen and men.

But of course, at the beginning it was Pilkington foremen and workmen working hard on shift work with their foremen and workmen with the Pilkington man taking the responsibilities for the job and training of his foreman and man working partner.

This was well acknowledged by the Saint Gobain people and near the end of the visit the foremen and men were given trips out to Cologne and one or two other places.

Once again the name Pilkington was being boosted in Germany through the successful results, loyalty and hard work of the Pilkington workmen.

The team returned home after 10 weeks in Germany, happy and satisfied with the job they had done.

Because of heavy demands now being made by float progress and licensing commitments increasing I will explain the position we are up to in 1965 as regards to the practical glassmakers.

(a) There are now three float lines working at Cowley Hill Works.

(b) Each float line has a senior foreman who is responsible for practical working and organising of materials, tools, etc — he works days.

(c) Each float line has four shift foremen, one for each shift, as they work a four set shift system.

(d) Each float line has four chargehands, who are capable of replacing the shift foremen for sickness, holidays, for licensing commitments, etc.

I will now explain the Float Line in three sections.

1. Furnace

2. Float bath

3. Lehr

1. THE FURNACE has on each shift, six men.

    1. One man for filling broken glass, which we call cullet, into skips.
    2. One man for tipping and feeding the materials into the furnace.
    3. One man crane driving.
    4. One man controlling the gas flames and temperatures.
    5. One spare man for relief periods and housekeeping with the shift chargehand keeping a watchful eye on furnace conditions and temperature.
    6. Two furnace menders, for three furnaces.

2. THE FLOAT BATH has on each shift five men.

    1. One man known as a spout operator controlling the glass flow from the furnace into the float bath and being responsible for width control.
    2. One man responsible for the control and monitoring of the tin temperature, bath electrical heating, atmosphere gases, all temperature and bath conditions required for good glassmaking, bath safety, pressures and dewpoints.
    3. One man continually keeping check on the float bath seal to prevent oxygen entering the bath plus little jobs for good housekeeping.
    4. One man at the exit end of the bath measuring the ribbon width as often as required
    5. One spare man for relief work and housekeeping.

3. LEHR

    1. One man to record the lehr temperatures and control as required, according to glass annealing temperatures, and observe for breakages.

This gives a total of 171 personnel, three Senior Foremen, 12 Shift Foremen, 12 Chargehands and 144 Workmen.

But in anticipation of licensee commitments, holidays, sickness and training, the total number of personnel was 190, so that the lines could be worked efficiently when there were teams abroad on licensee start-ups.

As the foremen and men were all working hard in the interests of the future success of the float process, flexibility in the learning of most of the different jobs didn't create any difficulty.

There wasn't much difference in the job pay rates, and as a man was learning a job or doing the job on a higher pay rate than his normal job, he would be paid the higher rate accordingly.

When the time came to pick start-up teams to travel abroad, this was not always as easy as it looked because:

(a) Some were not experienced or trained for float bath work and would rather stay on furnace work.
(b) Some had home commitments they could not leave.
(c) Some were quite content and happy to stay at home and had no wish to travel.
(d) One or two could not go because of health reasons.
(e) The three Pilkington float lines had to be run efficiently with fully trained, experienced foremen and men.
(f) In case of sickness or refusals for future heavy licensing commitments, it was policy to give as many men that were qualified a chance of overseas experience.

Having analysed all these points, Pilkingtons were very lucky as there was no sign of jealousy or discontent amongst the foremen and men as to who went abroad and who didn't. They were socially one good set of men, all happy working hard for the future. Still encountering hot heavy overtime and many-a-time encountering new working techniques and practices, assisting in every way humanly possible to improve and contribute, which they did to the success of float glass.

At this stage many of the foremen and men had accepted, as Mr Winston Churchill once said: "Blood, toil, sweat and tears". Really, they were the backbone of the practical working side of the float successes.

As all human beings are not made the same, one or two were now feeling the strain and showing signs of fatigue and cramp more often, when carrying out hot work around the float line, than they had previously, but they still soldiered on.

It was also noticeable that the wives and familes were experiencing this change, and even they carried on, accepting, it was a job to ensure float success and jobs for the future.

Team work and loyalty to job was magnificent, inside and outside the factory which was most important at this stage. Again a critical time in the early stages of licensing. God bless them all.

The licensing programme had now become a heavy demand on the foremen and workmen, as one can see by the number of float licences signed to date in 1965.

27.7.62	Pittsburgh Plate Glass
14.12.62	Glaverbel S.A.
14.12.62	Glaces de Boussois
3. 4.63	Fabrica Pisna de Specchi Lastre Colate di Verro Della
10. 4.63	Glaceries de St. Roche
19. 4.63	Libbey Owens Ford
6. 1.64	Vereinigte Glasswerke GmbH
6. 1.64	Compagnie de St. Gobain
6. 3.65	Asahi Glass Co. Ltd.
6. 3.64	Nippon
3. 6.64	Cristaleria Espanola
29. 7.64	Ford Motor Company
29. 3.65	Vidrio Plano de Mexico

Even at this stage various problems with float glass production were encountered and had to be solved by the Foremen and workmen.

All the 13 firms (in as many as seven countries) who had signed licences, all with different languages and environments, must have had complete faith in the quality of workmanship of the Pilkington workers.

With glassmaking being recognised throughout the world as a practical hard experienced workman's job, it was quite obvious, that the licensees would want proof of the fact that a normal glassmaker could be trained to operate and work a float glass line efficiently and effectively to make saleable float glass, and this is exactly what our foremen and men gave them the answer to, success, knowing our foremen and men would help and train their workforce.

This was a massive asset to Pilkingtons because, even at this stage, there was no training department capable of training practical workers in the skills of operating a float bath line and these men were now teachers to the world's practical float glassmakers, which, was really a massive job for them to willingly accept and at the same time doing their own work.

When I talk about teaching, this type of teaching is entirely separate to schooling, or university teaching and I honestly think many a psychologist does not understand how distracting this can become even for family life, unless he has had the experience himself.

The importance of the job, had for the past eight years, allowed many of the men less time at home with their families than they would have had normally, but with added licensee teaching and extra work, it meant that some of the foremen and men got even less time at home.

While the Pilkington Float team were in Japan, there was a French team of licensees in Cowley Hill Works from Boussois in France. Once again, the team of foremen and men who had been previously picked, had the job of training this team mostly by practical working methods.

The reader must surely realise now what I mean by heavy working and responsibility commitments because, to carry out a programme of work like this, many foremen and men had to work a lot of overtime covering for holidays, sickness, a team in Japan, and licensee training; plus three production lines working and development practices of thin glass making, were coming heavier and more successful.

The Boussois team came to Cowley Hill Works for a four week training period, and once again the Pilkington team of foremen and workmen was mixed with some who had had licensing experience, and some doing licensing work and training for the first time.

The same type of training and hard practical work was required as previously with the other licensee teams, but this time, the French team did not seem to be as enthusiastic in getting down to the hard work as other licensees, which made the training a bit harder for the foremen and men, but the French team received the same social welcome in Cowley Hill and outside the works as the other teams.

It was the end of January 1966 when the Pilkington foremen and workmen went to France to the small town of Boussois.

Boussois is situated approx. 3 miles from the tourist centre known as Meauberge which is Northern France, 3 miles from the Belgian border.

Maubeuge has a zoo, castle, good shopping centre and with

hotels, restaurants and bars. Unfortunately it was winter time which was dull and miserable, with most of the places closed.

The factory at Boussois had connections with Pilkington for many years especially with the grinding and polishing departments.

It was built on the banks of the river Sambre, and most of the materials for glassmaking were transported by barges which were were off-loaded by cranes into the factory stockpiles.

With Boussois being a small place there were no hotels and most of the houses had been specially built for the glassworkers of the factory.

The men stayed in Maubeuge and from the hotel they went by van or car to work shifts in the float factory.

Yes, it was the same again, hard work, overtime, plenty of responsibility, but a different working environment.

The toilets, showers and changing rooms were not up to English standards. Most importantly, as was well recognised at the time, it was not advisable to drink water from the taps.

This was a big disadvantage to our men especialy when it was very hot and they were sweating excessively. So the Boussios people had crates on the side of the float bath with bottles of drinking water for them; also, many crates of a low alcohol beer if needed.

There were a few small problems, mostly created by lack of experience, but in general the Pilkington foremen and men did a good job in the training, and practical working with the Boussois foremen and men on the float bath.

Many of the Boussois management could speak good English which was an asset to communications, and gave the Pilkington team encouragement in work and helped them to see what social life there was, which was very little with it being winter.

It was once again a complete change in environment the men accepted such as drinking water, French cooking and food changes, currency changes, hotel standards, language difficulties, but a good job was done at work and the Boussois management were very pleased and happy with the good reports of the men's work, and social behaviour. Another good contribution by the foremen and men to the success of the future of float.

In 1966 my line No. 3 was shut down for four weeks for a major reconstruction,

The furnace was re-designed to melt 2,500 tons of glass per week.

The float bath was made wider and longer, with a new designed carbon bottom.

When we started up again we had a new set of chemistry problems because we were now in new world with the carbon lined bath; also new temperature figures and new nitrogen and hydrogen measurements.

I am sure by now the readers will understand why I refer to the float glass line foremen and men as technical glassmakers.

They have had the honour of working with, and solving even some technical problems, as well as making them work in practice under their complete control which is one of the main arteries of float success.

Now I will turn again to licensing.

From 1965 to 1980 there were approx. 20 new licences sold.

To save the monotony of the reader reading a report about each of them, I will report about one in each country.

Because of float glass licensing international commitments, the foremen and workmen were gaining a great wealth of international knowledge which was vital to the licensee and Pilkington, in the accuracy and speed of success.

If we look first at one of the most important control of glassmaking which is temperature, then we in England speak in units of Centigrade, but in American and one or two other countries they speak in units of Fahrenheit.

Next we come to measurements again, here is another very important control in glass making which some countries speak or measure in units of feet, inches, yards or miles, while others speak or measure in units of millimetres, metres and kilometres.

In weight measurements, some weigh in pounds and tons, in some countries they use kilograms and tonnes.

Water measurements here again are different, some have pints and gallons, other countries have litres.

Yes, here again most of the foremen and men trained each other, with their opposite licensee partners to overcome the translation of temperatures, weights and measures, so they could be efficient at their respective jobs.

This was not easy, because in England we had not changed over to the metric system at that time, and there was a difference between the teachers and the pupils, our men being the teachers. The pupil was only interested in his own system of weights,

84

measures and temperatures but the teachers had to converse many times in both systems with different licensees in different countries.

By now the name of Pilkington was well advertised throughout the existing and the prospective float glass world, if only by the talk and hard work our men put into their training and practical work when in licensee factories abroad.

Yes it was a time when our competitors were looking up to Pilkingtons for help and guidelines. As we say a good product sells itself and the float line workers were the finest salesmen Pilkington had in those days. They were the key to the product.

Even at the airports, if there were women and children boarding an aeroplane with lots of luggage and any of our men were there, you would always find them either carrying the children, or the hand luggage up the steps of the plane to assist and help anyone who required it. It was their good way of life (down to earth men).

6.12.66	Sklo Union
1.2.67	PB Canada
29.3.67	V/o Technoprominport
7.2.68	Central Glass Co. Ltd
17.12.68	Glaceries de St. Roch
21.5.70	Combustion Engineering Inc
2.7.71	A.S.G. Industries Inc.
7.4.72	Vetreria de Vernante
3.5.72	Societa Italiano Vetro
23.2.73	Fourco Glass Co.
30.1.74	Pilkington Floatglas AB
8.5.75	Polimex — Cekop
29.10.75	PV (South Africa)
17.6.77	Turkey Sise Ve Cam Fabrikeri
20.10.77	Industreanlagen Import
16.11.77	Hankuk Glass Industry Co. Ltd
20.6.78	Pennsylvania Float Glass Inc.
18.1.80	Vitro Flotado
17.3.80	Cebrace
1.5.80	Taiwan Glass Industry Co.

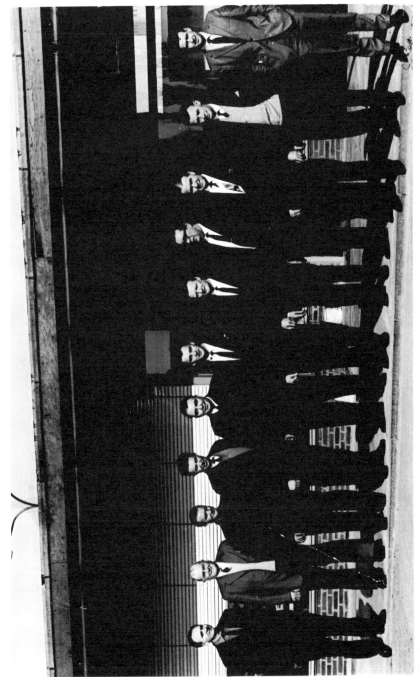

The boys in Germany.

11

CZECHOSLOVAKIA

I will move now to Sklo Union in Czechoslovakia, January 1970.

Here again, a team of two managers, four foremen and sixteen workmen came over for training. By now many of the problems of the earlier days, for example the production of thinner glasses, thicker glass, chemistry, bath sealing, speed, width, electric heating, ribbon control, they had mostly vanished. Also the foremen and men had already a lot of experience in training their opposite numbers in the licensee teams, which made the workload easier.

Having pointed the workload out there was still a language problem, as out of the team of 22 Czech personnel, only six of them could speak English, and all translations, whether in work or social mixing, became more of less reliant on at least one of the six licensees being them at the time.

The licensees were different to previous ones, for most ot them had not experienced the riches and homes of the western countries and they were humble. I could sense a feeling of inferiority especially on social occasions. The men did everything possible to make them happy and welcome by taking them into their homes and clubs.

Although the Czech team were staying in a good hotel with good food it was the simple social freedom of life in England which appealed to them most.

As one of the men said: we solve more problems at nights when we go to the fish and chip shop, because if you given them chips and fish in a newspaper with plenty of salt and vinegar you are their friend for life. The psychologists will never understand this.

There are many different classes of people in the world, and in many instances, confidences can only be built up by a mutual understanding of each others' circumstances, and using this understanding in a social, practical way. This is exactly what our men and families did, which ultimately contributed to the successful training of the Sklo Union team in England.

It was winter January 1970 when the team went to Czechoslovakia, the float line was built in the town of Teplice.

Teplice is situated approx. 10 miles from the East German border and at this time I would estimate the population to be in the region of 70,000—80,000.

The two hotels were low in standard in comparison to the hotels the men had stayed in before, this was another type of environment which was well below the western environments.

Before the men went out to Czechoslovakia everyone was well aware of some of the conditions they would encounter because of the political differences and poverty of these people. It was necessary to go out prepared as well as possible.

To help the men, Pilkington's issued each man with a good fur coat, hat, safety boots, gave them a few pounds to buy some warm underwear because of the very cold climate at that time of the year.

They also took out with them foodstuffs like soups, tea, coffee, chocolate, sweets, etc. Also, clothing for working purposes, like asbestos gloves, safety spectacles and any other protective clothing needed. Most important were the salt tablets to be diluted in water and drunk when sweating at work.

I remember when I went to Czechoslovakia in winter time we were met at Prague Airport and we had approximately 3½ hour journey in the back of a van to the factory at Teplice.

There was ice and snow on the roads, it was cold in the back of a van. We did call at a roadside cafe, but all we could buy was fruit or beer, and we were absolutely tired, hungry and cold by the time we got to our hotel.

Our first thought was for a good hot meal but the hotel kitchen had finished by 8.30pm, and all we could get were sandwiches and beer, and at 9.00pm there didn't seem to be anyone around.

The hotel was what we would class as a third rate one, but it was a matter of there being no better one in Teplice.

Next morning I was awaked at about 4.30am. I looked through the bedroom window and thought I had overslept or my watch was wrong because there were lorries, vans, trolley buses, and people all hurrying off to work with their food satchels.

For most workers normal starting time was 6.00am. We were due to start work by 8.00am and we went down for breakfast at 7.00am. It was a continental breakfast with coffee, no choice of food.

It was now we realised the difference, for there were no cars, no taxis to take us to and from work, which was approximately 1½ miles from the hotel. It was either queuing up for a trolley bus in the cold icy snow, or walking. Most of the time, it was walking.

The factory itself was in a built-up area. It wasn't a big factory but was many years old. No car parks, just bicycle stands.

As we went into the factory lodge there were two big alsations with a lady security officer and she pointed to a lift to take us up to the main office which was on the third floor. The building was four storeys high.

These lifts were open lifts (no doors) with the cages continually moving, going up, and coming down. It was a matter of jumping in and out as the cage arrived at the floor you wanted and amazingly I was told there were never any accidents, but boy you had to time your movements precisely.

As we went into the factory there were many communist slogans hung in many places on banners and one could immediately feel the political eyes of Big Brother everywhere.

When the Sklo Union men had to do any extra jobs which required overtime, the overtime payment for them came as a bonus not as an overtime general pay rate.

I remember one night, the afternoon shift, who were due to finish at 10.00pm had to stay overtime to do a special job. This job started at 10.30pm and finished at 1.00am. It was a hot job putting some refractories in the bath.

When the job was finished and the management were satisfied, each man then came into the manager's office and received the equivalent of 50 pence in crowns, which was their currency.

The manager told me that was their pay for doing a good job. I then asked him "Do they get any other payment?" and he replied "No". If they had done a bad job on overtime they would have got less.

As we were walking back to our hotel at 2.00am. because there was no transport for us, we notice three drunken men acting in an abusive way but the manager said "Don't worry walk smartly past them". The drunken men immediately behaved themselves and walked smartly and quietly past us thinking we were K.G.B. men. This was the type of discipline the police administered because they were ruthless with law breakers no matter who they were.

These people were poor and there seemed to be no class distinction allowed.

Most of the managers lived in small flats just like their workers did with very little difference in pay rates, and if the manager was lucky enough to afford a car it would probably be ten or fifteen years old.

Yes, they all used the same canteen, and the type of dinners every day consisted of boiled potatoes, suet dumplings, veg and gravy, and sponge cake and custard. The choice of menu was something they could not afford.

Safety First Regulations in the Glass Factory were minimum.

There was a lot of broken glass being removed by the workers using picks and spades, the workers were spading the broken glass into hand barrows.

None of the workers who were a mixture of male and female, was wearing any protective clothing, no safety spectacles, no gloves, no safety shoes, some were even wearing open toe sandals.

When I asked the works manager who came talking to me at the time why they did not wear any safety clothing when handling broken glass, he replied, we do not have accidents in this factory. If any of those workers who were gypsies cut themselves, they will go off work and by the time they are better again someone else will have taken their job, so they are careful and don't have any accidents and by gum they didn't have accidents.

I remember going to the works annual winter dinner festival.

We were told to be ready for 6.30 pm as it started at 6.30 pm.

There was a brass band playing waltzes and polkas all night. There were sandwiches and beer, everyone enjoyed themselves in their own customary way, but at 10.00 pm everything finished because they all had to get up early for work next morning.

The police were very strict on noise after 8.00 pm.

There wasn't many clothes shops but what few there were, good clothing was very expensive, and I am sure it was out of the reach of the majority of the people, but most people were always at work, and seemed always to be dressed peasant style.

The food shops did not seem to have a large variety of different food stuffs, but what good food there was in the shops went very quickly, for if you passed the shops early morning there was always big queues waiting inside and outside the shops as though most of the food was on ration.

At the factory our foremen and men did a very good public relations job as well as their own hard sweat, responsible jobs.

Crowns cannot be used as a currency exchange when leaving Czechoslovakia which meant our men had to use up their crowns and being the men they were, they spent a lot of time and money helping the Sklo Union workers and encouraging them to appreciate what a good process they were getting.

All this is another example of the necessary types of contribution the workmen did accept in the interest of the success of float glass and it is not easy to keep adapting to everyones different ways of environment especially when they are leaving a good home and family behind to do it.

I remember being in Teplice at one time when I myself was feeling afraid of the political situation.

There was a newspaper printed in English named the "Morning Star", of course, it was natural for any English man to pick it up at the hotel desk as free reading material.

This I used to do just like the other men did and it was interesting for several reason: (a) it was something to read, (b) it was the only way of knowing the current news back in England, and world news.

There was always one page of communist news, and this page published the names of the organisations in England who made contributions to the communist party.

Most of it could have been propaganda, I don't know, but it was amazing how many there were, even on our own doorstep in St Helens.

None of this bothered me, until one day as I picked up the paper, one of the men in a joke shouted, Hey, why are you reading the Morning Star, you are a conservative. Yes, at that time I was a conservative councillor back home in St Helens Town Council.

The man behind the desk looked up for he could speak perfect English and it was then I realised what politics meant to these people, because after than incident I had a feeling of being watched.

It was an uncomfortable feeling, I don't know, but I had a suspicion someone had been in my room other than the cleaner when I had been out at work, for I had that feeling when I walked into my room one night, I looked around, there was nothing out of place. No, I had not been drinking, but I was uneasy afterwards until I was back on the plane on my way home.

You have to experience some of the environments to fully understand what these changes for the men were all about.

It was very understandable why some of the wives and families were very frustrated when their husbands and brothers were going out to different countries. It must have been very hard for some of them to accept.

I had the experience of travelling in many countries during the war of 1939-1945 and my knowledge of people as more or less understandable and it was easier for someone like me who had already known international travel than someone who hadn't, to adapt to new environments.

Once again here was another massive contribution by the foremen and workmen and more so than ever, because of the political situations they were encountering which was new to us all, and they were the float glass practical pioneers in the communist world, and this had to be for the success of float glass manufacture in the communist countries.

Unfortunately the men had not been back home from Czechoslovakia for more than three weeks when they were called out on strike on 5th April, 1970.

12

1970 STRIKE

The strike action came as a shock wave to the majority of the float glass workers on the afternoon shift on Friday April 5th. It hit them just like the 1987 hurricane hit the South of England when the people were in bed and unprepared.

Yes, they were upset about it being forced on to them as quickly as possible, because some of the other stewards and workers requested the float glass men to down tools within a matter of minutes and walk away from their jobs.

This did mean that management had to shut down the float lines which is a very hard and tiring job but some of the workmen stayed behind to help in the closing down of the float lines, which was a big help in the interest of plant and personnel safety.

The float lines were closed down within a couple of hours and for plant safety reasons were put on a soak temperature of approximately 800°C.

There were many people who had theories and even wrote books as to why the General and Municipal Workers had decided to strike when they did, some quoted inter-union disputes, bad management, differentials in pay rates, bonus systems, you name it, but in the end the readings only amounted to there having been a seven week damaging strike at Pilkington, the press and television people had enjoyed themselves picking up anything from anything from anyone that would make exciting news and, as we know, those people are not interested in good people and good deeds, for they openly confess it is the bad news that sells and makes their jobs.

There were also experts from universities, schools of economics, all fishing around, clutching to any straws of any kind of scandal or rumour to build up a story so they could come up with the answer as to why this strike happened.

I don't know the answer myself and the only reason I can think of:

(a)   The march of time and education, because as time progresses, so does people's education no matter what class they belong to.

(b)   Automation was slowly coming into the factories demanding new environmental changes, which benefited some and not others.

(c)   The firm was expanding and investing with the profits coming in from the invention of float glass.

(d)   The G.M.W.U. were mostly the production workers and expected a better pay rise from the profits.

(e)   The Pilkington family directors were very close to the workers, and made a point of visiting and talking to them as often as possible when the Head Office was in Grove Street, and had a good working relationship both socially inside and outside of work.

     When Head Office was moved to Prescot Road this relationship began to diminish, but it was also a time when licensing and many other extra commitments called for more of their time away from the shop floor although they came occasionally but not as often.

(f)   It was also a time when a lot of new administration departments were beginning to branch out into little empires of their own.

(g)   There was a big intake of young inexperienced managers with their own ideas of how to handle shop floor workers.

I remember when I was on a foreman training course at Burton Manor College in 1960.

There were many foremen from different factories in the country on this course, and each day we had a full two hour discussion period on personnel relationship experiences with the unions and shop stewards.

*Curved facade of the
1939 Head Office
in Grove Street.*

*Pilkington Head Office
as it is today.*

One foreman said he had given the shop steward up as a bad job. When asked why he replied, well it is like this; the management allow him a free hand and are afraid of him, and everytime he passes my window he puts two fingers up to salute me, and, if there are any complaints he goes and by-passes everyone and goes straight to the personnel manager; the personnel manager calls the culprit and the shop steward into the office gives them a cup of coffee and biscuits while he has a talk with them, then he sends for the foreman, listens to the foreman's story, sends the foreman out when he has told his side leaving the culprit and the shop steward in with the young personnel manager.

Ten minutes later after personnel manager, the culprit and the shop steward have had a chat over a cup of tea, the door will open and out will come the culprit and shop steward, the shop stewards will walk past the foreman, put two fingers up to him and say won again.

Another foreman said we don't have any problem in our factory like that.

If a man has a complaint he uses the shop stewards' charter. The shop steward sees the foreman and most times the complaint is put right at foreman level, because, he is the man who understands the person and his job, and can compromise a peaceful solution which is in the interest of all, including the firm.

If the foreman cannot solve the problem then his immediate superior, who may be the senior foreman may solve the problem.

If the senior foreman cannot solve the problem then it is up to the departmental manager to solve the problem, for it is very dangerous for someone like a personnel manager to override foremen, in preference to building up his own image through a shop steward.

It is no good having a shop stewards charter if people are not going to work to it, for this is very dangerous to everyone working for the firm.

(h)   Finally, there was plenty of scope to examine job descriptions and pay rates which had been really neglected by both the Unions and Pilkingtons management before the strike.

If it will help I would like to give some personal examples.

In 1935 I was working shift work at the age of 16 years in what

96

was known then as the disc grinding and polishing department.

My first job was emptying two sand wagons per shift by spade, each wagon holding 20 tons of sand.

The sand had to be spaded by myself into a bucket conveyor which fed the grinding machines also I had to keep the rail tracks clean and tidy.

My 75p per week. On top of that we had a bonus which was cullet money those, days, which I remember, was even down to 1p to 15p per week.

After being on the sand graders for four weeks I then was transferred to the polishing side, what a job.

The glass was laid on a big circular table, the table was approximately ten metres in diameter.

To polish the glass the table was run on lines under four polisher heads.

Each polisher head had six revolving polisher blocks with a 1″ thick rough felt on, and each block weighed 1 cwt.

When the glass was in position under the polisher heads my job was to start the polisher heads revolving.

As the polisher heads were revolving on the glass surface, then to polish the glass it was a matter of feeding the correct amount of liquid red rouge on the surface of the glass, so the felt pads could polish the glass.

The feed was fed from above the polisher heads, which meant the liquid rouge was being fed from a tub which held approximately six gallons of rouge, and to keep this tub full of rouge it was a matter of me running up and down eight steps of stairway, with a three gallon bucket of rouge approximately every ten minutes at the same time keeping a close watch on the table for breakages.

If we had any breakages then the table would have to be stopped, extracted from its position and the polishing blocks would have to be scraped to clean out any broken glass in the felt, or if the felt was badly damaged the blocks had to be changed.

To change the polisher blocks was a hard dirty heavy job and it needed two strong young men to do it.

When the revolving table with the glass on had been removed from the polishing position, then it left a gap of approximately four feet from floor level to the polisher block.

The polisher block was held on to the polisher head by two nuts and bolts and by this time the felt on the polisher block was well soaked in red rouge which in total weight must have been approximately 1.25 cwts.

It was a matter of one young man bending down with his back under the polisher block, taking the weight of the polisher block on the back of his shoulders, whilst the other young man would unscrew and remove the nuts and bolts, and then between them they would remove the worn block and felt.

Putting the new polisher block and felt back on was a similar job but in reverse order, for the man who replaced the nuts and bolts, he would first of all set himself in semi-crouch position, hold the block and felt on his thighs, this would then be transferred on to the back of the shoulders of the other man who would take the weight of the block and felt, whilst it was being tightened and fixed into its working position on the polisher head.

Before the table was put back in to working position, we had to clean out the broken glass and dirty scummy rouge from the channels under the polisher floor base with brushes and spades, this was flushed away into a gully to the waste tips outside the factory.

The table was then put back into working position and once again the polishing routine began again.

Those days we didn't have any free issue of overalls for working in, we had to provide our own also to wash ourselves we were provided with paper towels, and a kind of very brown soft soap.

This soft soap did not always remove the rouge properly from our hands so we used to mix it with a bit of ash, which we had to be careful with, otherwise the ash would burn the skin and cause a skin rash.

The rate of pay for this job was again 75p per week with the 1p-15p per week bonus. (When I talk of 75p it was 15 shillings per week those days).

Because we had no proper cleaning facilities, for cleaning overalls, at work, many had to walk to and from work to their homes in dirty clothes mostly covered in red rouge.

There were three of us working on the same shift living approximately four to five miles away from the works, our only transport facilities was either by bicycle or tram car.

None of use had bicycles and when we wanted to board the tram car the conductor would say to us, no Red Indians allowed, only Cowboys, as we would dirty the seats with rouge from our

98

Disc Polishers

clothes, so this meant approximately one hour's walk to and from work each day, for e.g. when we were on day shift which started at 6 a.m. we met at our meeting point at 4.45 a.m. so we could be in work by 6 a.m. Otherwise if we were late for work the foremen may send us home.

I had been working in the disc grinding and polishing department for approximately six months, when I was transferred to the continuous grinding and polishing department.

My job still at 16 years of age, was exactly the same, on shift work having to spade two wagons of sand into a bucket conveyor, each wagon with 20 tons of sand in it and keep the lines clean.

The wages were similar, 75p per week but the bonus was very much higher ranging from 50p to 75p per week than in the Disc Grinding and Polishing Department.

After a month spading sand I was moved to the Polishing Department.

The job was much easier and cleaner, because there was no buckets of rouge to carry, the rouge feed was mixed centrally and pumped by pipework direct to the polisher block and felt pad.

When the polisher block and felt polishing pad needed changing there was no bending down and heavy lifting of the polisher blocks as we did in the disc polishing Department because the table was a flat continuous table about two feet high which we would easily drop the block on and remove more easily.

The continuous grinder and polishing machines were doing a similar job as the disc grinding and polishing machines except the disc was more labour intensive and dirtier than the continuous one, yet the pay rates were the same, 75p per week. This was when I first noticed the different pay systems.

No one seemed to bother about this because people were content to be in work and were quite happy working for Pilkington which was recognised as a good employer for many good reasons such as wages, recreation and welfare benefits, and that they would create as much employment as possible.

It so happened complacency set in and as I said earlier the unions had their inter-union problems and as the old saying goes it is the survival of the fittest and once a pay level has been attained by a strong section of people, there is no way the would let the lower paid people come up to their level unless they were

A line of continuous polishers for the processing of plate glass.

100

going to get to a higher level themselves.

Before I started on this book I had to make sure in my mind that what I am saying and writing about, at least I have had some personal and practical experience about.

I have given some of my experience in float glass production and international travel, so now as we are talking about the Pilkington strike which affected factories in England I will give you some of my knowledge gained on my working travels around them.

In 1949, 1950, and 1951 I went to Queensborough Sheet Glass Works on the Isle of Sheppy several times each year, for sometimes two weeks at a time, working and mixing with the G.M.W.U. people.

My job was to test the flows and temperatures on the glass furnaces, and work with their men, foremen and managers.

Naturally enough when having breaks or drinks at night, we did discuss rates of pay, working methods, Pilkington, Unions, and people in general.

With the works being on the Isle of Sheppy it wasn't a large works and most of the work people were quite happy in a little community of their own and all gave Pilkington a good name.

During the year of 1961 I visited Pontypool works and discussed furnace melting and oil firing, once again I had the opportunity to converse with the men over conditions and pay rates, and here again a small and happy community spirit was noted giving Pilkington a good name.

The Doncaster factory I visited many a time over a large number of years, as a matter of fact the people at the Doncaster factory at Barnby Dun, used to say to me, where do you belong to, St Helens or Doncaster because you are always here.

When any development work was in progress on the plate glass furnaces my manager would send me over to do the practical side of the job, sometimes even to do the technical side as well, and report back to him with the results.

Once again, I gained a good understanding working relationship with all the workmen in and out of work, and was satisfied Pilkington had a good name from the Doncaster workforce.

The three factories I have mentioned up to now had their own social and recreational facilities, and their welfare facilities.

It was different in the three factories, for the environment was different from working in St Helens.

The reason quoted by some of their managers, that the works

managers were more free to make local decisions more quickly because they were a long way from Head Office, and it was easier to allow the workmen little concessions with a smaller workforce than with a large workforce like we had in St Helens.

Of course the works managers were like kings in their own castles, but who could blame them, for they were doing a good job and getting good production with the minimum of upsets from anyone.

I have done plenty of work and social mixing in all the St Helens factories, as is well known in Pilkington.

Yes I had a three year spell on job ranking around the factories in England.

After the strike it was decided by the Directors to try and equal up the rates of pay of the G.M.W.U. workers by reducing the number of pay grades.

To do this, a job ranking panel was formed. It consisted of five G.M.W.U. shop stewards, three A.S.T.M.S. foremen and two Managers, this was the set up each time I was on it.

Our job was to go around different factories of the Pilkington Group in England, Scotland and Wales where G.M.W.U. were employed, and compare the grading of different jobs with the rates of pay for the respective jobs.

It was noticeable to me as a manager, that when discussions were in progress around the office table, after we had all seen the job, and spoken to the cutter, operator, cleaner, or whoever it was who's job we were evaluating that many were biased where jobs below their own job rate were concerned. For e.g. it was very hard to get people to agree that times had changed with new methods etc. and the person on the grade lower had now qualified for a higher grade rate equivalent ot his grade.

To be honest this happened with plenty of people of all grades and classes and as I said before it was a case of who had the most representatives at the meetings and I mean workmen, foremen and managers.

My other experiences were that I was a glassworker, I was a foreman and then a manager. In other words I had experiences from all groups.

Then there seemed to be a big change in policy, as the empire began to expand, and the workmen seemed to be less important, just like someone saying you stay there, you have done your job, now we want to take over from you on better and higher levels, starting with better rates of pay, although they had nothing to back up their potentials only a piece of paper from some educational college or school, which was far removed from the job they were coming into, and in many instances this was highly noticeable to the hard workers who were giving everything for the firms success in many departments.

I think this created a "could not care less" attitude on the shop floor and this is when trouble began by the division of thinking by the shop stewards.

As one manager quoted, glassmaking is no longer important, it is Sales, Personnel Training, and Accountancy that matters.

I replied that is wrong and he said, you wait and see, the workmen have already pointed this out, there will be no workmen in a few years time. I wonder if they will have PhD's and BSc's brushing up at treble the cost of a workman.

But he was wrong, Pilkington contracted the jobs out to cleaning agencies. etc.

Summing up I feel the majority of workmen were quite happy but the shop stewards had differences of opinions and this created a division among themselves.

Secondly, Managers and Personnel Management were having a power game between themselves.

The top leaders of the unions and the top leaders of Pilkington seemed to leave the problems to other deputies, quite rightly that is what they were paid for.

This meant there was a time loss being created, due to educational progress on all sides.

Personnel management are the only official people who could be blamed for this strike, they accepted the credit, so they must accept the bricks as well, "that is the name of the game", it was their job to see things like strikes didn't happen.

I don't think anyone was expecting a strike, especially Pilkington at the time it did happen, on April 3rd.

Apparently there had been a miscalculation in a bonus payment being paid, of couse this lit the fuse on the time bomb, which rapidly became the demand for an increase of 25p per hour on the basic rate.

The lines had been held on soaking temperatures during the strike, but there were many other checks and different procedures as I have quoted earlier that had to be carried out by the men, at a time, when their minds had not really settled down to the return to normal working; because while the strike was on some of them had differences of opinions, which led to a little hatred in one or two cases, whereas before the strike they were all best of pals.

It was really a damaging strike as far as confidence and morale were concerned causing families to turn against each other, of course outside interference from others like the press, television and silly rumours by many others didn't help because in most cases only the bad sides were being highlighted and the good sides were never mentioned, as seems to happen at these times, but we cannot ignore the fact that it does affect some more than others for a period of time afterwards and a little distrust creeps in the minds of some, where there is no need for it.

Pilkington was a family firm in more ways than one, because beside the Pilkington family themselves there were many generations of families employed by them, and this was one of the secrets of success, but now the paint crack was beginning to show in trust amongst some of the men.

I did have a little experience of this myself for e.g. one section of my family and relations were on the side of the G.M.W.U. workers who did not want to strike and the other section who did. And I as a manager was right in the middle, also it was the same for many others as I know of.

This situation can become very embarrasing because while the strike was on when I was going from and coming to work I would have to pass the picketts, sometimes I would stop and chat with them once or twice I have given them cigarettes, men who were my relations and work pals, I had nothing against them and they had nothing against me, on the other hand I would speak and help the other side as much as possible exactly the same way.

All this may sound very nice but (it is amazing as the police say) "everything will be taken down and used in evidence against you".

I am just trying to put over how hard it was, also, for some people to even see the other peoples points who were not on strike. But eventually these problems sorted themselves out as time went on.

Pilkington did lose orders while the strike was in progress, but also another hidden worry for Pilkington was the licensing commitments that they had signed, because if the strike had carried on for a longer period of time say many months, as some do, the licensees would have to wait for the float line workmen to return to work at Cowley Hill before they could start their float lines.

I am sure at this time that the eyes and ears of the glass world especially the Licensees were focused on the float line workmen, because, there was not another team of workers in the world in the Pilkington organisation anywhere experienced enough to go and take over the mens respective jobs as required, for float glass making at this time.

This may sound a bold statement to make but practical experience was definitely on the side of the workmen, because of the numbers required, and the efficiency expected, which in bulk only the workmen had at this time. Yes we did have managers and technicians in numbers, but there is a big difference in watching someone doing what seems a simple job, apart from the hot, frustrating, concentrating glass making side, then actually doing it yourself. As we say it is the drivers who drives the car not the mechanics, and the workmen happened to be the drivers (no disrespect to anyone else), but once again here was an example of the essential contribution needed by the firm from the workmen towards the success of Float Glass Licensing commitments by G.M.W.U. workers. Yes there is no doubt in my mind that during the six weeks the men were away from work that new policy decisions were being made for the future, to ensure that a stoppage of this type could not happen again at Pilkington.

In my position I could see that while some of the workmen were happy to be back working again, they still had their minds on differences of opinions that came up between workman, and workman, and were not noticing little changes that were slowly but surely going to affect them at a later date.

This stike gave the administration departments just the opportunity they were waiting for, to build up their respective departmental management teams, for they could see a big new Float glass empire emerging, throughout the world, and they wanted to be a part of it, and who would blame them? It was only natural for them to do this.

The managers and technicians from Research and Development Departments began participating more in some of the practical jobs around the float lines. Jobs like the preparation and setting up of the refractories, tin, heating, sealing, etc. They were realising that as time was progressing and when we had reached the ultimate on float practical development work, there would be jobs for them, at home, abroad and licensee work, again this was a natural thing for future progress.

None of the float line workers' shift job responsibilities were affected because, as I have said, these were jobs in their own practical grouping, which no one wanted to know of at this time.

It was also at this period that a big new float glass line was under construction at Cowley Hill Works which was due to come into production in 1972, which would mean we would have 4 float glass lines operating at Cowley Hill Works, meaning more workmen would have to be trained for this extra commitment and also licensee work was really putting a lot of pressure on the workforce as well. Yes, the shop floor were really playing a massive part in the success of float glass. What a headache all this must have been for some people at the top!

At this time also Pilkington had the world flat glass industry just where they could have asked for anything they wanted from them e.g. many competitors were very anxious for a float licence, many licencees were waiting for the building, commissioning, or start-up of their float lines. Many of the competitors were anxious to buy the float glass product itself. Although we did lose some customers during the strike, there must have been many a wasted opportunity to more than double full order books at this time.

As I said earlier in this book, a lot of the hard working foremen and men were brilliant and had first class brain power, and I remember quite clearly one of them saying to me after the strike was over, "This float process is just like driving a heavy loaded wagon up a very steep hill, struggling along in bottom gear, and after a few stops and breakdowns, it eventually reaches the top, and then the top gear eventually takes over, and cruises along on the level road in comfort, and what is more there is nothing we can do about it."

For the older experienced men and foremen there was a big change in the work environment, even on the float licensing side, to the noticeable effect of the terms of travelling abroad in float start-up teams, for example the terms of personal spend allowances, were not reduced but they were not increased in line with inflation rates. There was also a big tightening up by Personnel Departments on such things as overseas bonus time payments, and clothing allowances. The personnel management didn't appreciate what was being asked of these man and their families by the firm and the foreign licensees, and of how much money these start-up teams were making for the firm. Or did they?

I admired the float glass workmen and foremen because although these men could see a little into the future, sometimes different from what they had worked hard for, and expected for their families, nothing or no one distracted them away from their working responsibilities, whether it be in England or abroad, float glass production was their top priority.

Time had been progressing right from the start-up of the PPG line in 1963 and we had progressed with the production of thinner, and thicker glass, naturally our licensees were entitled to these benefits.

In the early years 1965-1967 when we were making thinner glass with the method of gripping the top and bottom surfaces of the glass by edge rollers in the float bath, and using the pull from the lehr speed, to thin down the glass thickness, which was a hot, concentrated, practical experienced job, in a few cases a number of our expertise foremen and workmen would work on shift work in the licensee' factory, supervising and training their opposite numbers. This was another added contribution to float success by shop floor workers.

The float line foremen and workmen's role was being increased, not only by U.K. commitments, but some of the licensees who had started float lines in the early days were now in the stages of requiring help in the commissioning and starting-up of their second float lines. This was at this stage, a float line production job, and a licensee request of course this only needed any experienced manager.

Developments in the Continuous Manufacture of Plate GLass

◄The Flow Process. Originally developed for the continuous manufacture of plate glass, the process was soon adapted for making rolled (seen here) and wired glass.

◄Continuous grinding and polishing. The rough plates of glass being laid on a series of continuous tables to pass under grinding and polishing heads.

▼Close-up of a polishing head.

Flying the British flag in Japan.

JAPAN

It was summer time 1965 when the Japanese team from Nippon Glass Company came over for training. Once again it was a matter for foremen and workmen, who had been chosen to go to Japan to train and even socialise with the Japanese, while they were training at Cowley Hill Works.

Most of the Nippon team could speak English so the translation problems were eased a little, except in Japan "yes" means "no", and "no" means "yes", which caused a little confusion when the men were trying to explain something about the process.

It was very amusing at times because most of the Japanese team were about the same height, most of them were wearing spectacles and everyone dressed in the same type of working uniform, and no matter who spoke to them, they would bow and give that courteous smile and nine times out of ten they would finish by saying "Yes" when they really should have said "No".

They were hard working and very thorough, writing down everything they were told about the job and asking many questions about past and present problems on the float bath and even asking for repeat demonstrations where they could be applied.

All this may seem a big asset to the training programme, but at the same time it became hard and boring for the foremen and men because, many a time when the men were working hard and sweating maybe on overtime, and even tired, a little

109

Japanese would come up with his book and pencil and ask him for a running report of everything in detail on what he was doing and why.

But of course, the men did work with them as much as was humanly possible, training them in practice, as well as theory, and outside working hours the foremen and men took the Japanese team to the clubs, pubs, their homes etc. and as with other licensees Pilkington allowed expenses for both teams to visit Blackpool and North Wales.

This again was a massive stride in the international industrial relationship which had to be formed for float success world - wide.

The Pilkington team consisting of two managers, foremen and men similar as previous start-up treams, went to Japan in November 1965 for start-up.

The Nippon float line was built in a more or less average size fishing town named Maizaru which was approx. 20 miles from Osaka, also Maizaru was a Japanese naval base.

Maizaru did have shops, bars and restaurants, just like an average town in England, the food was Japanese style mostly fish, rice and salads. Beer was easy to purchase, also there were restaurants where English food could be obtained like chips and steak and fruit.

It was amazing how many Japanese could speak English. I was at the home of one of the Japanses one night, he had four children between the ages of 4-14 years-old, and everyone of them could speak English. I asked him how this came about and he replied: "Well our children automatically learn the mother tongue, so in Primary school we teach them the Western language which is English, for it is easier to teach them at a younger age, with songs and nursery rhymes".

Once again the Pilkington foremen and men did a very good job, worked very hard and adapted themselves to Japanese climate, working and social conditions and after 10 weeks came home to prepare for more hard work and adventures in the float programme with another well satisfied customer on the list of successes.

It was in 1972 I was asked to go to Japan to commission a big new float line for Nippon and then to stay on and supervise the start-up of glassmaking and remain until saleable glass had been achieved. It was at Cheba on Tokyo Bay,

This is a story I won't forget. I remember I received my money, airline tickets and vouchers neceessary on Friday. Also when commissioning I used to take out with me, a specification manual, and a check list, so that if the lincesees had made any mistakes in the float bath construction or services then it would be easier to point out any mistake, and have it rectified before the commencement of glassmaking, because if there were any doubts in my mind, I could always refer to my specification and cross check to have the problems rectified.

Of course, the licnesees could please themselves, for it was their float line and their money that was involved, but if the licensee strayed away from the Pilkington recommendations, and did not make good glass, well that was their problem, and they fully understood the consequences, so it was always a matter of the full weight of responsibility being put on the shoulders of the Pilkington man and believe me, out in a foreign country on your own as I was, is when you realise it more than anyone back home does, but of course, it was my job which I knew and fully accepted.

I was due to fly out to Japan on the Monday, so on the Sunday I did mypacking, and after packing my cases, I left out my float line specification manual and check list, to have a read and confirm everything.

I was sat ont he settee in my lounge on the Sunday evening reading the specification when my wife's sister and her husband came in and asked if we would care to go out with them for the evening.

Naturally I said yes, so I put my specification manual under the cushion on the settee thinking I would put it in my brief case when I came in later.

On the Monday morning there was a car to pick me up at 6.00am to take me to Manchester Airport for a connection to London. Of course, we are all human and it was always all rush at that time in a morning, especially on these types of occasions, making sure you have everything apart from what is sometimes most important. My wife said: "Now you are sure you have everything you need" I said yes love, gave her a kiss and I was off on my journey.

When I got on the plane at London it was a Japanese Airline Boeing 747. I got a window seat which I always asked for, because I enjoyed flying, especially on my own. I would like to sit quietly watching places and people, and a window seat is the best place to do this on a plane.

111

After taking off my shoes and putting on a pair of slippers I asked the stewardess for a drink, when I got the drink I was nice and comfortable and ready for an 8 hour flight to Anchorage in Alaska, so I opened my brief case to read up my specification, but, I had a nasty shock, when I realised what I had done, for I had left my Float Line Specification and all my notes back home under the cushion on my settee.

Just imagine a man of my calibre on his way to do a highly valuable, technical, engineering, electrical, scientific, building, chemical, political checking and glassmaking responsible job in a place like Japan, for the Japanese were known to be so thorough in every little detail, no matter what section it was, and here I was going right in the firing line without a bullet, on my own, no-one else to blame, or ask.

The flight to Alaska seemed like eternity, I worried myself all the way I didn't have any food or drink.

We had a 2 hour stay in Achorage Airport, so I went to have a walk around, and at one end of the airport building there is a huge white bear which had been embalmed and put on show. It stood about 8 or 9 feet tall, and just against it I noticed a big queue of Americans, so I thought I will see what they were buying. They were buying little tins of something, for a dollar a tin, and it was then I spotted a lady with three children, she was English and was upset, and one of the children was crying so I thought I could help, and I asked him what he was crying for which the lady appreciated. He said I want one of those tins they are all buying, so I thought I would buy him one. Yes I did, I was another sucker, they were tins of London Fog, but oh boy that really put my mind back to where it belonged, and I said to myself stop worrying you silly fool you know your job practically and theoretically, why worry about the licensees. This young lady going out to Japan on her own with three little children needed help, for she was going to join her husband at Osaka, who was working for the firm of Wimpy, and she had never travelled in her life before, so I said, "Come on kids, we will go for some ice cream."

When we boarded the plane again I was amazed to find that this young lady and her children were sat in the seat behind me, and they were terrified of flying, and most of the passengers were Japanese so that did not help the situation, but what upset me most was the fact that I had been full of my own importance and I had not even noticed them on the seats behind me in fear

112

with no-one to help them by talking to them.

Yes it was a different flight for me from Anchorage to Tokyo, the children kept me awake and happy, and the lady felt more comfortable for it sure was a God send to us all, and I forgot all about float glass making.

When we got to Tokyo, her husband was waiting for her, and she introduced me to him, and he thanked me for being a help.

My next problem was to find my courier, because when anyone arrives at Tokyo airport it is very complicated e.g. I was told to look for a small man wearing spectacles carrying a white flag.

When after check-out I was going down the escalator into the arrivals hall, there seemed to be hundreds of Japanese, all small, all wearing spectacles, all dressed the same and all carrying white flags, and of course with me concentrating on the English lady and her children it delayed me a few minutes, anyway not to worry, my courier found me.

My courier happened to be a manager who I had never met before who was to be the engineer responsible for this new float line, his name was Mr Mitsuno who later became a great friend of mine.

After our little acquaintance meeting his first reaction was, please Mr Grundy will you kindly come to the factory tonight as we have many problems.

Tired with no sleep for 24 hours and a bit of jet lag, I had to say yes, for he was so polite and humble with his request.

It was 10 p.m., Japanese time, we got in a taxi, it was a dark, wet, windy night and off we drove to the ferry because the quickest way he knew was by ferry across Tokyo Bay. I tell you it was a very rough crossing actually frightening, there was no-one on only us, and it had been specially reserved.

Tiredness, jet lag, and now sea-sick, everything a worried man needed to make him crazy. I had to laugh about it, it was really unbelievable I don't know where I got the stamina from, only God knows.

The ferry was a boat about 50 ft long and it bounced up and down and we were told to wear life jackets. It took approximately 3/4 hours, which at the time seemed 10 hours.

We got off the ferry, and a taxi was waiting for us, it took us to the factory, which was another 15 minutes ride in the wet and windy night, and although the weather was wet and windy it was warm with it, and I would have given anything for a good cup of English tea, but no chance that night, it was either Japanese green tea, beer, water or lemonade, so I went for lemonade.

When we drove into the factory I was taken straight to the Float Line and I was requested to leave all my belongings in the taxi, and examine the float line with the float line manager and their chief engineer.

After a good one hour checking up on the float bath section, and noticing the danger points, I asked the manager to hold the bath temperatures as they were for 24 hours, because what had happened owing to the inexperience, as the float bath was warming up the expansion of materials was moving the wrong way, and a lot of adjustments had to be made to the services around the float line.

The Japanese management knew they had made a big political mistake by not waiting for me, to check up personally before commencing to warm up the Float Bath, so my request was granted for they were trying to gain a couple of days on start up time.

It was early morning when I got to my hotel which was about the size of the average English pub, about 8 or 9 rooms, three of them set up Western style and six of them Japanese style. Western style means toilet, bath, shower and wash basin and a good bed, Japanese style is more communal for bath, washing, toilets and they sleep on a mat on the floor.

I had no complaints with my room it was comfortable and very clean and had a window view of Tokyo Bay.

After a good nights sleep, I woke up about 8 a.m. to a glaring sunshine, I unpacked my case, had a shower and went for breakfast at about 9 a.m. Yes I did manage to get a good cup of English tea as I had asked for the previous night, for this is one speciality about the Japanese if you are their guest nothing is impossible.

At 10 a.m. Mr Mitsuno came for me in his car, which was only one mile away from the factory and as we drove in the factory I could not help but notice what a beautiful place to build a float glass factory.

The sun was shining, not a cloud in the sky. It was a big new factory with a beautiful garden design, and goldfish pools to the front entrance of the main office. The factory buildings were well spaced out with plenty of concreted road space in between building sections, with the whole factory having a sea-shore background of Tokyo Bay.

Everyone was wearing the same grey overall uniforms from works manager to shop floor worker, all females wearing the uniform, white blouse, grey skirt, white socks and white gym shoes and everyone so polite with each other, what a marvellous impression I got, and there I am my sweat shirts and no specification or notes.

As I walked into the float bath area I suddenly felt very confident and strong in mind, about how I was going to handle any situation that came along.

When commissioning a float glass bath prior to glass making my responsibility was to check all services, such as gas, water, steam, air, electricity, atmosphere gases, tin loading equipment etc. they were ready, and also the services were free from the movement of heat expansion as the bath warmed up.

Next all bath steelwork and refractory superstructure is completed as per specification agreement.

Check all steel expansion movement discs, pads and rollers etc. around the sides, top and bottom of the bath steelwork.

All datum and expansion measuring and recording instruments are ready.

Check all bath welding positions and where not to be welded until hot, to seal up temporarily.

All temporary steelwork in a controlling position to keep the bath roof in line with bath bottom when warming up.

I knew all these jobs as I had done them many times previously.

What the Japanese engineer had done was to forget about the steelwork controls under the bath and the bath was not being allowed to move freely, also a couple of the service pipes had been welded where they should not have been etc.

This gave me the opportunity I needed, I asked him, have you been working as per specification? He said, "Yes Mr Grundy" so I said, "Are you sure?" "Yes Mr Grundy" so I replied, "Right, come on, let us go to your Drawing Office, and check up on your specification and drawings, and you can show me what you have done."

We went to his office, he produced his Pilkington specification and necessary drawings and I proved to him where he had been making mistakes, he was full of apologies, he not knowing I did this for my benefit mostly, so I could have a final check myself to make sure I had missed nothing out, because my specification was back home.

About 4 p.m. the Line Manager said the Works Manager wanted to see me. At that time I was doing some measurements under the Float Bath and I was a bit grubby looking, with a dirty football jersey on.

I cleaned myself up to present myself more respectably and 10 minutes later we were in his office.

The works manager's office was beautiful, there was a waiting room with huge settees and large arm chairs, glass tables and every comfortable convenience, overlooking the sea shore, and inside his office was even more comfortable.

As I walked in he shook my hand, but I noticed he did not bow like all Japanese do when greeting any visitors.

He was a very big man and straight away I sensed here is a hard, firm, working man.

His production manager who was with him was on the small side, and he did not look Japanese style, he reminded me of Peter Lorre the quiet actor detective, a type who did everything quietly and effectively.

I had never met them or heard of them before, but they knew all about myself and my Float experiences.

The works manager first apologised for bringing me straight into work and thanked me for doing so, instead of going to the hotel after a long tiring journey. He told me he was worried about the construction movements of the float bath.

I assured him no harm had been done that we could not rectify, and also this type of problem I have known and experienced many a time, so not to worry everything will be O.K. We shook hands and that was it, off I went back into the factory.

When I got back into the factory I had a discussion with the float line manager about his float bath personnel and he told me some of them were from the other Nippon float line at Maisaru, but of course at this stage, even they were not experienced in the commissioning, warming up, and starting up of a float bath because they had only seen it done once before, and it was done by a Pilkington team, but they had enough knowledge to be of great help.

I gave the instructions for the warming up schedule to start again as from 10.00pm that night. It was 8.30pm when I left the factory to go back to the hotel, and when I got to my bedroom

I just flopped down on the bed and fell fast asleep until 6.30am. the following morning, Wednesday, and I was still tired.

Once again the sun was shining, I had my breakfast and went into work at 8.00am as arranged because that was the starting time for all management and office workers.

It was about 7.50am when I got to the front entrance of the factory and all the office staff and managers were stood in small groups. I thought they were waiting for the doors to open to let them into work, but at 7.55am someone blew a loud whistle and each group lined up smartly into physical training teams, and seconds later the music for physical training began playing through the tanoy system.

One of the managers said: "Come on Mr Grundy, join in", I replied "Do you want to kill me before I start work, or after the job is completed", because if I had joined in that morning I am sure I would have dropped with heart failure or something. I don't think I had one ounce of energy in my body at that time.

They always had massed physical exercise every morning at 7.55am to 8.00am and every lunchtime at 12.55 to 1.00pm. and after I had been there a couple of days I did eventually join in with them each time, because by then my body and system had settled down to normal. The best of it was, I really enjoyed the five minute non-stop exercise to music.

This type of exercise for work preparation was very common in Japan, whether it by industry, shops, petrol stations, in fact in every place of work you would see them at their specified times doing exercises for a few minutes.

These exercises were the beginning of a team spirit between all the workers and bosses, which is essential for success, and helped everyone to start work with a clearer, healthier mind than they would otherwise have had.

On Wednesday I had more like a rest day at this period of time for the bath was at a low temperature and I did a one hour check around all datum and measuring points at 9.00am and 4.00pm and I sat looking at drawings and graphs, etc., explaining the necessary future preparations and expectations of commissioning control.

It was 6.00pm when I got back to the hotel, so I had a bath and decided to go down to the bar for a drink before dinner because there was a manager taking me out for a meal and he said he would be back for me at 8.00pm.

As I walked into the small bar at about 7.30pm. I heard

117

someone shout, "O.K. Tommy Grundy" I looked around and sitting on his own was a Frenchman who could speak perfect English, who I had met and worked with a couple to times on licensee float lines. I went over to him and said "Hi John. What are you doing here?" and he replied "I have come fishing, what you doing Tom?" I replied I was on holiday, of course we both knew different.

John was a constructional engineer and he worked for a firm named CNUD. Wherever a new float line was built the licensee would in most cases ask for the CNUD annealing lehr. It was John's job to commission the annealing lehr, and this would be at the same time as I was commissioning the float bath. However, I would stay longer than him because my job entailed glass making afterwards, but I knew that for the next week or two I would have someone in the hotel I could converse with whenever we had time to meet, because at these times his job called for plenty of overtime and so did mine.

At 8.00pm the Japanese manager came along to take me out for dinner. He took me to a large bowling alley which had a large restaurant split up into two sections, one Western and one Japanese style. Of course we went into the Western style restaurant.

A table had been reserved for four people and as we approached the table two Japanese men came up to me smiling, they shook my hand, and bowing said, "Good evening Mr Grundy" in perfect English.

During the course of our meal, we had a good conversation about food. I was brought fruit juice, steak, chips, salad and fruit, coffee and cream crackers and cheese. They had different Japanese dishes. I said to them how do you know what I like and they replied "We heard about you going to a Japanese Banquet and not liking Eastern style cooking. You had fruit and nothing else only beer, so now we make sure you get Western style food, steak and chips".

After the meal had finished the manager said to one of the men "You go now", and the man politely and happily excused himself for having to leave the company.

The three of us then had a game of ten pin bowling, and afterwards we went and sat at a table near the bar. We had one drink and the manager said to the other "You go now" and again the man politely excused himself.

After he had gone I was a little curious as to why the two men should have to leave in the middle of a party they were enjoying. I asked the manager and he replied: "The first man to leave was a foreman and he was happy to come and join us for a meal and then he leaves, no offence, it is our custom. The second man was a junior manager, so he had a meal, a game of bowls and one drink, then he leaves, no offence, it is our custom."

This is when I realised that although the great team work is there in the factory, the difference in rank is accepted outside the factory.

Yes, I had a good night and it was a change, I got back to my hotel about 11.00pm and there was John sat on his own listening to an Hawaian string band, so I had a drink and a talk with him until midnight.

Both John and myself knew that as from Thursday we would be busy at work approximately twelve hours a day and possibly more and although we were in the same hotel we never conversed or met inside the factory. This may sound crazy but he had his job to look after and I had mine and when you have a big responsibility, especially away from home, nothing must be allowed to distract you from your job. So at midnight we said goodnight and off I went to bed.

Thursday I was back into work at 8.00am and it was now that the float bath really needed careful attention because as the bath was gaining in temperature, the refractories and steelwork was beginning to expand at a faster and more dangerous rate.

My first job would be to examine all the progress charts, graphs, any remarks made by the night shift, all temperatures, etc. This would take approximately one hour.

Next I would personally measure and check every nut, bolt, joint, measuring gauge, etc, under the float bath on top, all sides, every refractory, this type of thorough inspection took about two hours of non stop, dirty hot work each time and it was my responsibility to see nothing went wrong.

When I was not doing my site expansion checking I was fully engaged on future preparation work, making absolutely sure that all services, equipment for tin filling, etc. even to the personal requirements and know how were being discussed and trained.

This is a time when every type of question is put forward by the Licensees, especially the Japanese whether it be technical, practical , or even political. Believe me, you are the Pilkington Managing Director on site, as far as they are concerned, but to tell anyone back home this, they would laugh and say he is only Tommy Grundy, a glass man, because when you return home you get behind the masses of really important necessities, when the chips are down if you have no academical qualifications to your name.

For the next four days as the bath was steadily increasing in temperature, my job was becoming heavier, hotter and more time and emphasis had to be put into everything for we were now in the dangerous period. This meant I was working approximately 12-14 hours each day, only going to my hotel for a sleep and a meal.

I had been working in the factory about eight days when I got very bad backache. It took me about five minutes to put on my socks and lace up my shoes. I must have got a chill in my back with sweating, and the type of back straining I had to do under the float bath, checking measurements whilst it was hot.

I did not tell anyone how much pain I was in, it was a matter of working hard, accepting all my responsibilities then going to the hotel and off to bed.

After three days of terrific back pains, I told Mr Mitsuno about my problems and he said: "I could see something was wrong when you were climbing around the bath doing your routine checks".

He made arrangements for me to see the doctor in the works surgery. The doctor gave me a good examination — I mean a good one — he did everything, bar hit me with a sledge hammer, then looked at me and said "You'll live" and smiled. He told me to come for another check up if the pain persisted, he also gave me some white and green capsules to take three times a day. I did take the capsules as prescribed and after a couple of days my back pains were a lot better, but I didn't go back to see the doctor again.

It was a time when the bath was at its hottest temperature 1,000°C, and the Japanese management were getting very anxious because they had one or two little problems of their own at the furnace end, which ultimately put more extra work on my job, because at this critical time, not only does the float bath need 100 per cent attention, but the canal and the spout and lip have got to be accurately measured and assembled, ready for installation after the correct amount of tin has been put in the float bath, and this responsibility comes in the same category as the float bath which was mine.

The hot glass flows from the furnace through the canal and then passes under a gate, or known as a tweel, down a refractory lip onto the molten tin and the position and measurements of the spout lip in relation to tin must be accurately set otherwise glass quality may be affected.

For the next three days I worked approximately fourteen hours per day working, sweating, supervising, instructing, advising and taking all responsbilities of tin filling which is a dangerous job and the setting and warming up of the spout lip; but the Japanese being excellent workers, gave me every confidence and encouragement I needed for success as the saying goes "they gave me all my own way and a bag to put it in."

This again meant all work and little sleep, and I remember the day before we were due to start glassmaking I had gone to bed about 11.30 p.m., had a restless sleep, and I got up at 6 a.m. feeling tired and weak.

When I was in the bathroom having a shower, I started trembling and my first reaction was I am having a heart attack and I was afraid, but what was really happening was, I wasn't having the shakes it was an earthquake tremor, and by gum was I relieved when I found out for the building was shaking for a second or two.

On the morning of the start up of the float line I was in work at 6.00 a.m. doing all my normal routine checks etc. and having discussions with management.

It was arranged to start glassmaking at 10.00 a.m. The Japanese management put a big ribbon around the spout area, and spot on 10.00 a.m. the High Priest came along in his robes, cameras etc. he said prayers then cut the tape, and we started glass flowing at 10.15 a.m.

There seemed to be a quietness about everything with about twice as many people participating in the start-up as to what we would have had in England, but everything went very well, and oh boy what a relief for I had said my prayers also.

It was about 6.00 p.m. when I got back to the hotel, I had a bath, a meal, a drink and went back into work at 9.00 p.m. to check up and again everything was working well according to plan.

Next morning when I went into work, I was really happy for everything was going great, and the glass quality was improving rapidly, and by 8.00 p.m. that evening they were making

121

saleable glass, I went back to the hotel and met my French friend John who had just completed his job of commissioning the CNUD lehr and so we both had a celebration drink or two before going to bed.

Although we started making saleable glass within 36 hours after starting up the line, it was of an inferior quality which is something they could sell to a customer who did not require glazing or silvering quality glass.

This again meant a lot of glassmaking experience and know how and hard overtime being worked for the next three or four days for we had one or two chemistry problems and distortion problems.

As we improved the bath seal, and found the best temperature targets, suitable for good float glass making, we did after three days make glazing quality, which the Japanese management were highly delighted with, as a matter of fact I got that many bows, smiles, and handshakes I thought they had mistaken me for their High Priest who cut the tape at the start-up ceremony.

The day we made saleable quality glazing glass, the works manager sent for me and told me how happy he was and that he wanted me to join him and his production manager for dinner that evening.

At 8.00 p.m. they both came to my hotel in a taxi, had a drink with me and then off we all went to Cheba.

When we were in the taxi on our way to Cheba the works manager told me of the strain it had been for him being responsible for a big new multi-million pound factory, relying on a new era in glassmaking.

He said to me what would we have done Mr Grundy if we had not made good glass? I replied they could only sack us both, and he smiled and so did I and that was the beginning of a good night.

I know it is easy to joke about anything after the event, but I knew what he had been going through, before good glassmaking was achieved.

On the way back to our hotel after the dinner he said that Mr Mitsuno would take me to Tokyo next day and show me around all the interesting places in Tokyo.

Next morning Mr Mitsuno came round to pick me up at 7.30 a.m. and he said first we must go to the factory and do our exercises, and the check up if everything is alright and we are still making saleable glazing glass and if we are still making good glass we can go to Tokyo. They were, so we caught a train at 10.00 a.m. to Tokyo. By the way this was on a Saturday.

It was a hot morning and when we got to the station, the station was over-packed with people waiting for the train to Tokyo. At 10.00 a.m. the train pulled in the station, my friend said keep hold of me or you will get lost in the crowds. Yes we were all stood up packed like sardines, and to an Englishman in these circumstances every Japanese man looked alike, for everyone of them seemed about the same height, and all wearing white cotton short sleeved shirts.

The journey took about 60 minutes, we stopped at about 10 stations and each time we stopped the people would just hurry off, and hurry on the train otherwise they miss the train. I did lose sight of my friend once with the bustling and shuffling around, but again he could not lose sight of me which I realised after, because I was the only Englishman on the train.

When we arrived at the Tokyo central station I was amazed at the size of it for there was a never ending flow of passengers coming and going all the time with trains approximately every few minutes to the surrounding outskirts of Tokyo.

Apparently practically everyone uses the train services in Japan at this time, and when I got out of the station, I understood why. The roads were absolutely full of cars and taxis and on a Saturday it was quicker and safer to walk around Tokyo because the Japanese drivers seemed to have a law unto themselves (the survival of the fittest).

My friend asked me where I would like to visit first and I said, I would like to see the Royal palace.

Yes we went there. It was approximately 10 minutes walk from the station, and when we got there I was really tired, of course I didn't say I was, but around the Palace there was a kind of moat and one section was absolutely beautiful with the Japanese cherry trees in full bloom.

The water was full of beautiful fish (golden carp) huge ones they were, I would think some were about 2 ft. in length. I sat on the wall really admiring them and I could have sat there all day but we stayed about one hour.

Next we went for a meal in the Ginza shopping centre, but it was in a huge hotel, and it was noticeable that all the big hotels in Tokyo have their own shopping centres inside the hotels.

I am sure the Ginza is about one of the finest shopping centres in the world. It has everything to cope with for any type of foreign visitor, and every class of person "rich or poor" and it is so clean, and organised with beautiful buildings, chandaliers, revolving staircases etc. I would say it was the best of London, New York and Paris put into one area, it was a real eye opener for me, of course there was the Japanese poorer sections as well. After the meal we went to the top of the tower building to look over the sites of Tokyo, and it was from this position I had a view of the City, Airport and the Bay.

At that time they were building a wall in the sea in preparation to reclaim more land space from the sea.

I really did enjoy the afternoon sightseeing, and I noticed once again that although there were millions of people milling around shopping etc. the politeness and manners shown by everyone, even on the stations, where there were absolutely thousands of them hurrying for trains, and on the packed trains themselves.

That evening I was invited to Mr Mitsuno's home for dinner. It is the Japanese custom to have their wives cooking and waiting on and this is exactly what happened. I asked Mr Mitsuno could his wife join us, but no, even when going out at night it was the same he told me, they stay at home and the man goes on his own, I noticed this seemed to apply to nearly everyone I met in Japan.

The men would go to the gambling halls playing I think they called it Pershinca. In the gambling halls there would be rows of machines, the type were you put in the little silver balls and the ball goes round and down past the obstacles, scoring points at some of them, and for score points more silver balls would drop out, and then they could be exchanged for money, this type of sport and gambling seemed to be their favourite past-time.

On the Sunday morning we went into work later, 9.00 a.m. (no exercises that day) I stayed in work until 1.00 p.m. because they were having a distortion problem with the glass and I recommended some cooling changes, then I went back to the hotel for a meal and a rest. It was arranged that the manager would come for me at 7.00 p.m. so we could go back into the factory again and check the results of the recommended changes I asked them to do. There was little improvement so I recommended to go a stage further in the same direction and leave it overnight.

It was 10.00 p.m. when we left the factory, so the manager and myself went to my hotel had a drink and a chat about working conditions and then I got to bed about midnight.

Monday morning I went into the factory at 8.00 a.m. did my five minute exercises. The glass had improved tremendously and I was happy, so was the works manager. We had a nice discussion, and as we could both understand and agree my job was now completed, so I decided to leave on Wednesday.

Tuesday morning I went into work at 8.00 a.m. for a final check-up. Everything was excellent they were making float glass good enough for silvering quality which is the top quality.

They booked me a flight on Japanese airlines to leave Tokyo at 8.00 pm Wednesday.

After lunch I went back to my hotel, and I spent the rest of the afternoon packing my case etc. At 8.00 pm three Japanese managers came along and asked me to go to a Geisha party. At the Ghesia party it was a matter of sitting down cross-legged at a small table filled with food, Japanese style, eg. raw fish, fruit, rice-cakes, bits of beef, salad etc. with plenty of saki and beer and while the feasting was in progress there were Japanese girls giving a dancing display, singing and playing music. It was a good experience and I enjoyed it, and we had souvenir photographs taken.

It was arranged that Mr Mitsuno would pick me up on the Wednesday morning at 9.00 am to take me to Tokyo.

When Mr Mitsuno and myself were on the station platform waiting for the train to arrive, he told me he had orders to take me to the Ginza shopping centre and to buy my wife and myself any presents I wanted. The works manager and all the other managers had made a collection for the presents in appreciation of the good hard work I had done for them and their comment was, I was a brilliant engineer. I said no, just a glassmaker.

When we were in Tokyo my first thoughts were to buy some presents for my family, which I did. After I had bought what I wanted, Mr Mitsuno took me to camera shop and bought a beautiful cine camera for me as a present from management then he took me to a jewellers shop and bought a white gold wrist watch for my wife, a present from Nippon Glass.

We then went for a good meal (Western style), had a couple of drinks and then off we went to the airport to arrive at 6.00 pm so I could book in for my flight at 8.00 pm.

Yes, I flew out on time on a J.A.L. 747 to Anchorage, it was a seven hour flight.

The Japanese had booked me in at a hotel in Anchorage so I

125

could have a days rest before flying on to London.

At that time, Anchorage was just a small town at the foothills of the mountains on one side and the sea on the other. I remember getting there early morning, I had two hours sleep in the hotel and then decided to have a walk around the town.

Actually there seemed to be nothing there only one main street, a few restaurants and bars and a huge village green surrounded by a small community housing estate.

In the evening I went on the village green for a walk, which led down to the sea shore.

On the village green there was a concert in progress which was being given by the American Airforce Band, and for an occasion like this in a small place like Anchorage, the whole village turned out to listen to it, and I think there was approximately 300 people in all.

Next morning I woke at 8.00 am to catch a plane to London, another JAL 747 at 10.00 am, but when I got to the airport there was a flight delay and the plane left at 3.00 pm.

This plane did not go to London but to Paris, I then had to change to London and arrived in London at 6.00 am on the Friday morning this was due to time changes, by putting the clock back twice.

When I got to London the customs officials examined my presents, I told them the camera and gold watch were presents given to me by the company I had been working for and I showed them the receipts but they still made me pay a lot of duty on them.

I got the 9.00 am flight to Manchester and there was a works car waiting for me to take me home.

The works car got me home about 10.30 am. I got my luggage out and off he went back to work.

I knew my wife was on holiday at Blackpool that week with my family as previously we arranged, it being school holidays. But what I found out was that I had no key to get in my home so I had to get a ladder out of my garage and force open a bedroom window which was the easiest one to get into my home.

My wife came home on Saturday. On the Monday morning my wife and I went shopping and in Woolworths we saw some Japanese Dolls, made in Japan, exactly like two dolls I bought in the Ginza and nursed them all the way home from Tokyo on the planes so they would not get damaged, and lo and behold

126

the same dolls in every way were cheaper to buy in St Helens.

What a trip, all in the interest to the contribution of international float glass success.

Yes I did go out to commission and start up a few lines, we did have a licensing department and a commissioning experienced manager, but his commitments were so great, other float glass production line managers were called on to help out as required.

Just before I finish on commissioning and starting up of float glass lines there are a couple of real down to earth know-how experiences I had to make decisions on and face up to. The two Flachglas lines at Gladbeck in Germany which now belong to Pilkington.

I was asked to go and commission and start up the first one known as Gladbeck One. Gladbeck is a small village on the outskirts of Gelsenkirchen, Germany.

When doing my final check-up I realised that the end of the bath, where the glass comes out to go into the lehr, was a little too wide for glass safety entering the lehr, so I had to design some side tiles and have them fitted into the hot bath just before start-up.

The next one, when I commissioned the second line two years later, I think it was about the world's biggest at the time.

We had one or two little differences in bath design and when the bath was hot and filled with molten tin, I checked on all measurements and found at the end of the float bath the section where the glass comes off the tin over the lip was 6 mm too low.

This meant that the bath at that end had to be jacked up 6 mm before we could put more tin into the bath for good glass making.

Now having to jack up a float bath while it is up to temperature is a highly technical know-how engineering job in itself, plus the fact that we had nearly two million pounds worth of molten tin in the bath and a mistake by cracking a weld could lead to a multi-million pound loss of plant.

Yes, this had to be done. I phoned my manager in St Helens and cross-checked with him as to whether or not I should go ahead and do the job, as I was the only responsible person who had actually seen and done this type of job before, who was at Gladbeck at this time. He had confidence in me being able to do the engineering job efficiently and safely and gave me permission to go ahead with it.

127

I did have a Research and Development technician with me at the time but his job was to check up on glass faults and this type of work was not his responsibility, it was all mine.

The works director was a very nervous man about having to have the bath jacked up.

I had a meeting with his managers and engineers. It was a Saturday afternoon and he gave them specific instructions that they must do everything I requested, nothing more, nothing less.

We spent all Saturday afternoon freeing and unwelding all the bath services, and anything that would hinder or damage the float bath or equipment during the jacking-up period.

I knew I had taken all types of responsibilities in my time but really this was the greatest of them all; boy, I must have checked and cross-checked everything over and over again three or four times.

I reported to the works manager that I was ready for jacking up the bath. I told him we would leave everything until Sunday morning so that we would be fitter and fresher to start jacking up the bath.

At 10.00 am on Sunday morning I gave everything a final check to see everything was loose and free for bath movement, made sure the emergency services were ready and had a little meeting with the engineers on the jacking-up procedures.

When I was a young foreman I made a mistake of taking notice of someone else when I was a little in doubt. My manager said to me, "Always have confidence in yourself and if you are going to get fired for a mistake, make sure it is your own mistake and no one elses." I had this in my mind at this time and the thought gave me every bit of confidence I needed for this responsibility.

This job had to be done methodically with very careful checking of the welds each time a move was made and it took several hours. The works manager was under the bath with me all the time and every now and again he would walk away and I actually heard him saying, "Please God help us, let everything go all right. It did, thank God; I was also saying my prayers, but silently.

This is another instance where heavy responsibilities have been taken and done successfully in the interest of Float Glass by non tradesman or academically trained glassmakers many miles away from home, for there is a massive difference between a crowd and a lone person, only the actual experienced know this.

14

FAMILIES

In this book I have often referred to Pilkington being a family firm, which it was.

There were generations of Pilkington's and in each family, different type of responsibilities were handed down provided they were worked for because they were good workers.

If we go down the scale and look at Sales Accountants, Engineers etc, right down to the shop floor workers we could always make the remark, "Like father, like son". Following in his fathers footsteps.

I have heard many people say today there is nothing like that in Pilkington any more, maybe they are right, or maybe they are wearing blinkers, and can only see, and say, new technology has done away with everything. But I know of new technology in glassmaking even today which is requiring a lot of hard sweating, practical, experience work having to be done by similar people like I have been quoting but on a development scale.

There is a family history about float glass. I don't think anyone is aware of up to this present day, at Cowley Hill Works, and it concerns my family which is an old Pilkington family.

My history is well known so now I am going to tie up the oldest and most efficient Float Line in the world of today with one family. Yes, I feel it is part of my family. CH3 was the very first float line designed and built as a complete new float line at

Cowley Hill Works in 1962.

The first float line started at Cowley Hill Works in 1957 but that was a conversion on the old CH1 Plate Furnace and Lehr. CH3 is the only line in the world that I know of that has made thin glass, thick glass up to 25 mm, Antisun glass, grey and bronze, Spectrafloat, Reflectafloat, Camelion and now Low-E glass.

This line has been the workshop for practically, if not all, every type of glass made by the float process in todays world. It has more chemistry changes, more load changes, more different products, more different types of equipment and needs more hard work and practical attention than any other float line in Pilkington or anywhere else in the world as I know of today and trained every licensee. Other big UK5 and CH2 lines we have e.g. produce approx. 5,000-6,000 tons per week of clear glass, driving along comfortable in top gear on the level.

CH3 has to keep going up the hill changing gears for each project that needs hard, complicated attention at around 3,000 tons per week needing more attention.

CH3 is the family float glass line in Pilkington I would say CH2 and UK5 are its sons. Now we have spoken about the line itself, let us look at a family that has come along with everything that has had a big influence with every type of work whether it be practical or development or managerial on CH3 line from the start up in 1962 to this present day.

In 1961 I was appointed the Senior Foreman for this line, Lord Pilkington lit the burner and I placed it in the furnace which I still have a photograph of. In 1962 I started the CH3 Float Glass Line up. I remained with CH3 until I was transferred to assist in the preparation for CH4 conversion for a Float Line, of which I was promoted to the manager immediately after start-up.

I was only away from CH3 Float Line for a period of 20 months before I was brought back onto CH3 December 1964 as the float line manager, I remained in this position on CH3 line until 2 years before my retirement in 1979.

My son-in-law was a manager on the sheet glass furnaces, and when the sheet glass furnaces were closing down he was transferred to Cowley Hill Works to learn Float Glass making.

He had been at Cowley Hill for approximately four years when he was put with me on CH3 line, two years later I was reminded of my age, and my son-in-law took over the CH3 as Line Manager. That is one family tie up with CH3 which is

130

*The lighting by Lord Harry of
the First New Float Tank
C.H.3, 1962, the best
and oldest line in the
world today.*

unique in Float Glass.

Now let me give you another which is my son. He started in the C.H. Laboratory as a lab boy, 16 years of age in 1960 and at times came to CH1 float bath doing bits of laboratory work, like taking glass samples.

Later he was transferred to the float pilot plant research and development work, and was in with all the new development experiments with float glass.

One of the first glass coating experiments we did on Float Glass was done on CH3 line.

This was known as Spectrafloat, there was a long period of hard, hot work done by the Float Development Department who were based at Lathom, my son was in that department as a technician, he worked hard on this project and was a key man on site working. Yes he knew hard work, and his chemistry.

Spectrafloat was a success and he went abroad a couple of times with the Spectrafloat job.

Next we had a chameleon glass, which was a patterned top surface coated glass this was not a product that has a sales demand, but once again he did the necessary development, practical and theoretical hot work to make a success of the project on CH3.

Following that we had another top surface coated glass, which is a very good successful sales product known as 'Reflectafloat'.

One again he was a key worker on the theoretical and practical sides of this job on CH3.

We next have the glass of tomorrows world, the low emissivity glass, which is developed on CH3, which my son is a prominent key figure on in every stage of the experiment including the hot work. His name is on 2 of the Patent documents for this success.

On CH3 the Antisun glasses, Bronze and Grey are also manufactured.

I can also recall the days when we had an undercleaner at the end of CH3, those days we had to underclean the bottom surface of the glass. My twin brother who was then a foreman in the Grinding & Polishing Department was also the foreman in charge of the CH3 undercleaner, later he went to work for Pilkington in Canada.

Right from the very beginning of the working life of CH3 Line up to the present day, CH3 is and has been a big part of my family, and other glassmakers families.

Yes, my family has monopolised the control of its working life in many forms of work including administration and personnel on CH3 line, because since 1964 when I was promoted to Line Manager on CH3; the Line Management has been in my family — first me, then my son-in-law, no other line manager named as CH3 line manager to 1989, because CH3 is still in the building space that was allocated in the early days and therefore has not got the same amount of extra open spaces as UK5 or CH2, the conditions are much hotter and more uncomfortable to work in, also with having more equipment for more types of glasses, and experiments, more men are required for this purpose, which means it is much more easy for anyone who wants to find any faults with the glassmakers, than it is on a big line were there is only wide open spaces and everything in top gear and less men, less equipment and less work. Here again (disc grinding and polishing as to the continuous grinding and polishing.)

But coming back to the Float Line workmen and foremen, they also, have ultimately fell into line with each new project that has come along and played their respective required parts which still contribute to the Float success story.

CH3 has also been the guideline to the flat glass market of the world, according to what is going to be the next product.

Whilst we are on about families I can say that with my present service, my twin brother and I have over 100 years service between us for we both started work at Pilkington when we were 14 years of age.

I know and appreciate that in Pilkington there are many families in various works and departments who have similar records, for example, there were the two Owen twins who recorded 100 years or more between them at Sheet Works and it is all these points that highlight a family firm.

It is also the family at home that plays a big part as well, as we all know, and it is through the combined work, loyalty, and family trust that was one of the biggest contributory factors to the success of the Pilkington Glass Empire.

With the Float Process especially in the earlier days it was a matter of every time any part of the process had a little mishap the men, foremen and myself would be called into work even as much as twice in the same day, but what a disturbance it was to the families, I know many a time the phone would ring as much as two or three times during the night, and disturb everyone in bed, and then it is hard to get back to sleep afterwards, the wives would complain about being tired. One night when the phone rang my wife had got tired and I was out, and the foreman rang about three times in one hour, on the third time the foreman said to her, what should I do? So my wife said, "Put the tweel down and clean the bath out." and he did. I am sure with the involvement of family life to the extent as did happen on float, the wives should have got disturbance allowances, or bonuses for their dedication to Pilkington and their hidden contributions to the success of float glass.

A team set to go behind the Iron Curtain.

15

HIDDEN ASSETS

The float process was licensed by all the major glass companies throughout the world in every part of the Globe, North, South, East or West it was just like a huge hurricane, sweeping away every glass factory in its path and replacing with new float factories. I believe in the industrial revolution we often read or hear about, this, was only a small matter in global eyes, as regard to the float glass revolution.

When we talk about hidden assets, many people think in terms of money, accountants, economists, back room whizz boys etc., but these people have greater advantages than the hidden assets who contributed so much to Float, for they have educational advantages, they get bigger rewards, and with the unfair system of percentages, they ultimately outstrip all the things that made it possible for them to achieve their ambitions.

So now let us have a look at the other type of hidden asset the lowest paid and least financially rewarded, in this case, the Float Line Glass Worker.

We had several men who some people would class as uneducated, silly and irresponsible, but these were the type of men who could be relied upon when there was hard hot work and dangerous jobs to be done.

I remember very well someone sometime or other would say to me, we cannot trust such a man, or such a man, to do that job or whatever it was, and I would reply, "Why not? Who else have we got?" and at that time we didn't have anyone else, but they had the guts, loyalty and down to earth common sense that was needed from them in the emergency periods.

Let me give some examples. If and when we had trouble on the Float Bath, many a time it affected the furnace to the extent that it would be necessary to stop feeding the frit and cullet into the furnace which would mean the feeding machine would have to be withdrawn and the temperatures readjusted.

But with the emergency on the Float bath many a time important points like furnace feeding would be forgotten temporarily once in a while, and it would be all hands as many as possible working hard around the float bath and suddenly the foreman or myself would remember, what about the furnace feeder, and the next thing we would know is one of the furnace men would be at our side saying "Eh Tommy I have took feeder out is it all right?" Another would say, "I have adjusted temperatures, is it alright?" I would say, "Thank God for that", and then they would stop overtime working on any other job, and even their own job whichever was required from them.

This is a different picture from the wise guy who would do nothing only say no one told me to take the feeder out or adjust the temperature. Oh yes, we had the slow, and the smart, but they all completed a very effective team we needed them all.

There was another man who was a gambling collector, who was a tremendous hard worker and a real encouragement to other workers to work hard, and very loyal and conscientious in his job, and would work overtime, and he must have been a brilliant accountant as well, for he was a marvellous hidden asset.

Many of the men who wanted to place a bet on the horse racing would go up to him while he was working and say, "Jim here is my bet on such a horse, at such a time," and Jim would say, "go and put it in my jacket pocket, it is there hung up in the cabin," and if he needed change, he would say, "it is in my jacket pocket take it out."

Next day Jim would pay out to anyone who had winning money to come back in a similar way, the trust was really unbelievable, it was a real credit to men, and many times I have heard men say, "I was tired, but I came to work to place my bet, or collect my winnings otherwise I would have had one off."

Here was a (worker, an accountant, and personnel officer) all rolled into one, what a hidden asset he was.

There was another man who was a rough character, but had the biggest of hearts of anyone in need. He had a very important job those days of just standing at the end of the Float bath for the full shift of eight hours or more if needed watching for glass breaks and occasionally measuring the glass width and it was in a very warm unhealthy atmosphere.

This man never once left his post only for his meal break, but he always had his pal sat along side him, a big black cat. When it was his time off work we never saw the cat, but no matter what shift he was on, or if he was called in for overtime, the black cat would be at the works entrance waiting for him, and it would walk there with him when he was going home, and wait until he came back again.

Believe it or not, he spent plenty of his money buying the best of fish for this cat, and joking I wonder? He would say, "I had to come to work to feed my cat," also this man came along with suggestions that helped to cut down the cost of measuring sticks at the time, by recommending a fire resisting coating on the wooden measuring sticks.

We had a bath operator who was a big asset in the float entertainment line, he was a very good pianist and also had an accordian player, whenever the men needed a refresher, or, when licensees needed entertainment he would always oblige by playing his piano accordian for them, for a good get together sing song, also some of the mens wives would make a hot pot supper to supplement the entertainment.

Those days we used to get people coming around and standing around the tank or the float bath when hot heavy work was in progress and many a time the spectators got in the way of the worker, but one of the foremen was an expert at shifting them, for he would have a red hot bar and as he pulled it from the furnace or the bath, he would knowingly sling it down on the floor near where they were stood or, if he had a hot gas burner in hands, he would turn round with it and point it towards them no matter who they were and in an apologetic way would ask, sorry was you saying something?

We must have had a player for every position on the field, right up to the departmental manager Celfyn Thomas, for I remember one of the crane drivers did something wrong one day and damaged the crane on the hot end of the furnace, and Celfyn was absolutely brilliant and his sympathy's were always on the side of the workman, but this day he was really angry,

137

and he came to me in a temper and said, "who is that character up there in the crows nest?" I said, "who do you mean Celfyn?" he said, "him up there in the Crows Nest, Oh!" I said, "the crane driver," he said, "yes bring him into the office." I said, "if you sack him we have no crane driver this afternoon," he said, "I don't care I'll sack him." I asked the crane driver to come in the office who in general was a good worker and he was upset, and I was a bit worried myself, as to what would happen, because at that time it was not our policy to sack anyone or even suspend anyone, because we had no one else to replace them by and I must confess it was our policy to give everyone a fair chance. We needed them all.

When we were in the office Celfyn shouted, "shut the door," I thought here we go, we are for it now, he looked at me, looked at the crane driver and said, "that was a very unfortunate accident, I don't think it was your fault, but be careful in the future," and as the crane driver was trying to crawl out under the door, (as he remarked to me later), Celfyn suddenly said, to him, "oh by the way I have been observing you for a long time, would you be interested in learning the Chargehands job," he replied without thinking, "yes," and he was off like a shot.

When he had gone Celfyn said, "well what do you think?" He smiled, I replied, "what a relief, we will have a drink afterwards" for we both knew in our hearts the men were very near and important to us, although being human beings at times we did have our awkward rough words to keep the records straight.

The men never let us down at holiday time, Xmas etc. Once I got a phone call one Xmas Eve, 2 men came into work worse for drink, the foreman said, "what shoud he do?" I replied, "use your own discretion."

When I went into work Xmas day, the foreman said, "I let them stay, and they had a sleep for a couple of hours in the cabin," but by midnight they seemed sobered up, and both were filling the cullet skips and brushing up, but if I had have sent them home we would have had no one to do these jobs on Xmas Eve. He was inbetween the Devil and the Deep Blue Sea, but the foreman was appreciated by his men afterwards, and as he said, "if a good man falls once in a while we pick him up providing he does not keep deliberately falling." We wouldn't get away with this today.

Yes we even had a good natured chap in the float managers office. This man he was very efficient in a very peculiar way, for example if the Float Manager wanted anything in a hurry, he would ask his clerk to do it, of course the clerk would then nip into the office next door which was the Plate Glass Managers office, and borrow anything asked for from a drawing pin to the glass table top. He had this vice versa game going for quite a while, for he saw no harm in it, as he used to say to them, when they were angry with him, and they were falling out, each manager accusing each other of using each others office equipment, and either one manager or the other would say they would sack him. The clerk would say, "look here you chaps you are working for Mr Pilkington just like me, and there is no harm in using each others things, he pays for them."

Sometimes he would lock the office door and used the phone, keeping the managers waiting outside, but he was well liked by all, and he would do everybody a good turn by innocently robbing Peter to pay Paul, nothing was too much trouble for him to do. It is all the points which seem to some people to be silly and simple that is many ways, took away, many hard working pressures away from everyone which helped people to keep both feet on the ground from the top to the bottom while the struggles of the float plants were in progress.

Where there is hot work and hidden dangers like furnaces, hot molten tin, and gases and glass, success do not always come without one of two accidents, and I look back now and think we had more than our share of accidents in the run up to the success of Float Glass.

Maintenance workers on a hot tank repair.

16

INCIDENTS

One of the first was when we were transferring some hot refractories from one furnace to another, the wheel of the carriage carrying the hot refractories accidently caught the oil pipe leading to the furnace, this fractured the oil pipe and as the oil spurted out it ignited on the hot refractories and one of the men nearest to the hot refractories was badly burned and was in hospital quite a while and need skin grafts.

Another was when there was a repair on one of the Float furnaces one of the tank menders was crushed with the crane which he unfortunately died later.

We were doing a hot job on the furnace when one of the senior foremen slipped on a red hot hook which penetrated and burned his bottom, and when he was taken to hospital to have it attended to which required burns treatment, and stitching all the foreman could think about was getting back to work to carry on with the job. Of course, he could not return for a few days.

I remember when we had a tin leak at the front of the Float bath, myself and another foreman was trying to stop it by plugging it with a water box, at the time we did not realise the hidden dangers of hot molten tin, and as the hot tin run out of the bath it came in contact with the damp concrete on the basement floor below, this created steam, but, the steam was trapped under the tin which caused an explosion, this actually blew this foreman and myself about three or four feet away from the job, but I was more fortunate than the foreman because he was nearest to the blast, but we both finished up on stretchers at the works surgery suffering from shock. I was alright and fit again the next day but later on the foreman had to be moved off the float process for he never seemed to be as fit again and he was a very strong, fit man before the accident. As a matter of interest later he had a pacemaker fitted to help him.

Of all the float line glass workers and foremen who worked right from the start probably up to the first 10 years, I honestly don't think I know of anyone who escaped either a scald, burn, cramp or gas headache at some time or other during that first 10 year period and heat fatigue was accepted as a regular day occurrence.

I know of men who still have their problems with the cramp twisted fingers through handling hot heavy iron bars, which we used when we had trouble in the Float Bath.

Talking about family troubles, one foreman met an American lady when he was on the first float start up in 1963 in America and a couple of years later he went back on a float glass improvement and while he was there they got married. They both returned to St Helens and started a family, happily married. The foreman was in his early 50s when he began to have problems with his health, eventually he became worse and died at 58 years of age leaving a wife and children.

There are other float workers and foreman who didn't reach the age of 60 years before having illness, and dying before reaching the age of 60 years. The number of fatalities seemed incredible for one department to have. What the causes where I really don't know, but I am sorry that these hard workers did not live long enough to see and enjoy the fruits of their efforts.

On the float lines practically every job came under the heading of hot work, and most of our protection came in the form of asbestos. No matter what we handled was hot, so we always had a pair of asbestos gloves on our hands, our protection from the heat and fire was asbestos. Boarding, asbestos cloth was used to plug up fire leaks and gaps. Some other parts of our protective clothing like suits, hats, and veiling to protect our faces, had limited amounts of asbestos in them.

To put it blunty the men and foremen were eating, sweating and wearing asbestos and without asbestos we would not have done our jobs efficiently.

We were issued with clogs for footwear and I have known

times when doing hot jobs on the furnaces that the oil in the leather has got so hot that the oil soaked through to the skin and caused a burn blister on the foot, yes I have these blisters myself.

For eye protection we were issued with safety spectacles. The protective materials I have already explained are normal for glassmakers, but we then have the float bath. For protection against tin, gases, and electrics this is where caution and experience played its part.

When we were doing alterations and having to do hot tin draining; in the first few years the tin draining was a very dangerous job. The method was by valve and tube. As the hot tin was being controlled by a valve on the side of the bath, the tin was flowing through a tube which was heated by gas burners, just enough heat to keep the tin in a liquid flow, and the hot tin came from the tube into a mould, and when the mould was nearly full, one of the men would pick it up with the tin still in hot liquid state, and put it at one side to cool off, and another man would have put an empty mould under the tin pipe. This method was hazardous, and dangerous, and uneconomical, because of tin spillages and time. I did introduce a machine to make the job easier, safer and more economical.

After reading this book, some of the readers will wonder why it was possible for Pilkington to have such a good set of hard working loyal servants at a time, when hard work and loyalty was an absolute necessity in the early stages of the Float Glass Invention?

There is a well known phrase that seeing is believing which no one can deny.

I have see the Float Glass workers respect and team up with each other to the extent of working an extra hours overtime without payment to assist in each others beliefs.

It so happened that a large number of our foremen and men were devoted Catholics and they would always go to morning mass, sometimes off night shift, or before day shift.

With the men working plenty of overtime, which was very often, it was common for a man who had been working night shift, if he was asked to stay on longer, for him to ask one of the other men to cover him for approximately one hour while he went to early mass.

This the men would do willingly, knowing full well that the man would return to work immediately mass was over fully refreshed for more hard work. Here was a workers privilege that

I do believe would not be tolerated in industry today.

One of the foremen, who was a big hearted, very hard worker, jovial, and had a great understanding of men, happened to be a strong devoted Catholic and I can honestly say he was well liked and appreciated by everyone for his personality.

I think he was about the biggest man in the department, he wouldn't hurt a fly, but he strongly objected to anyone eating meat of a Friday.

Those days men used to bring their food into work, if it was cooked meal they would put it at the side of the furnace to warm up, or cook as required.

If any of the dishes had meat or bacon on them on Fridays, he would tell the owner of the meal, in no uncertain terms what he would do with his meal, if he caught him cooking meat or bacon again on Fridays, and believe it or not he would take a running kick at it, and kick the meal under the furnace.

All the men on his shift took it all in good part, and fun, and accepted it, so Fridays for that shift was a jam butty day, as the lads say.

Yes common sense and good moral standards are the fruits of Christianity which Pilkington was founded on.

The team at an International airport.

17

INTERNATIONAL METHODS

I have spoken about the humerous side of the hidden assets, now let us take a look at the assets from the serious side.

The majority of glassmakers had been war trained as to the real facts of life like: self discipline, physical fitness, a human understanding of people in all walks of life, and most important the security of job and family.

Because these men travelled around in a happy team spirit, they were very conspicuous, which gave many people of all walks of life easy access to talk with them, which was a much needed Public Relations exercise for the Pilkington invention.

The men would talk and advertise Pilkingtons, and be proud of the fact that they were part of the success of the new glass making process, but at the same time they never divulged the actual process itself. The secrecy of the Float process was a code of honour they kept and guarded at all times, Oh yes, these men had put far too much hard work into the process to see it freely given away.

This was not always easy for them, because whilst waiting in the airport buildings, and during their plane travels, they would come into contact with many business people, people who were very anxious to know more about the process, and times have been known, where some of the business men have shown willing to explain about their own business trips.

It was amazing to learn of the numerous ideas of British origin that were being marketed around the world in the 1960's and 70's, for it seemed that the British industrious people were leading the world on 'know-how' and development work. I could give a never ending list, e.g. Glass, Engineering, Chemicals, etc. even down to Fertilizers.

I remember on one trip to Japan, one business man was questioning one of our glassmakers about the Float process, and it became embarrassing for the glassmaker, so naturally enough the glassmaker change the subject, by asking him, the business man, about his trip to Japan and what his product was. Quite politely he replied "I am employed by Fisons and we are marketing a new fertilizer to the Japanese market.

Yes it is true the best product for the job, was always the best seller, but in many products, the life of the product is soon ended and bettered by another kind of product.

This has not been a feature of the Float Glass product, on the actual glassmaking side.

The type of improvements on the original Float glass have been on the cosmetic side, like surface coating, etc., which are still mainly Pilkington Development projects.

The glassmakers were the real concrete foundations of the Float glass industry and have a lot to be proud of.

Yes, the basic principles of Melting, Forming and Annealing are still in evidence all over the world, and have been for the past thirty years of so, and I do believe as an experienced glassmaker, this pattern will stay with glassmaking for many years to come, because this experience cannot be bought or made flexible overnight as it is a skill in its own right.

Another great asset was family workmanship and here is an example: One of the Senior Foremen had a son who was a Foreman, his nephew was a Chargehand and another relative of his was a spout operator, yes we had many Uncles, Fathers, Brothers and Nephews working in different jobs and shifts on the Float production lines.

Some of the industrial experts would say that this was not a good thing, for good results, but I will explain why it was a great asset to the success of the Float process.

With being in a new trial and error development world, we had to have people who understood glassmaking, and these glassmakers did.

Because of the many types of failures and little numbers of successes, every detail had to be carefully monitored and

146

recorded, but where and how? Yes we did record a lot on paper which makes good reading material, but many a time it was in the glassmakers mind which banked a lot of the information which is normal with a practical workman.

With the process being a 24 hour continuous shift process, some of the experiments carried on through maybe one, two or even three shifts and this is where excellent liaison had to be carried out, and this is where family unity excelled.

For many of the glassmakers who were experiencing new problems, it was not easy for them to always write the results of their observations down on paper, or even talk about them at the time of happening, because of confusion, tiredness, or some political reason, but they would register what happened in their minds, and at a later time, maybe at home or over a pint of beer, they would discuss the findings amongst themselves and no one else.

There were no working secrets, they worked as a Team, and I honestly believe that if we had not had this family, friendly atmosphere, there would have been plenty of back biting and hiding of important facts, for the Promotion Race.

There is a Proverb: 'United we Stand — Divided we Fall'. Here is the proof, and there is no better relationship than Family relationships.

Another great asset was the Pay Structure.

With the glassmakers being members of the G.M.W.U. this was a big asset to the firm, because the Float glassmakers were so few in the minority in numbers, that nothing could be done, unless the majority got a similar pay rise, this was accepted by the glassmakers, but reluctantly.

It was very interesting to see how our competitors, the Licencees, set about arranging their own new rates of pay for their glassmakers.

Many a time Licencee managers of different nationalities would converse with our glassmakers, their various jobs and rates of pay, so that the Licencee could set a similar pattern back in their own country.

They would also enquire about other peoples wages in the glass industry and the cost of living in and around St Helens.

The amazing outcome of it all, was that no matter which country I visited the Float glassmakers throughout the world were paid on a similar pattern as ours in St Helens, taking into account the various standards and cost of living, in each of the different countries, e.g. a high cost of living equals a high wage, a low cost of living equals a low wage, but the definite Float pay pattern was world wide.

Ravenhead Works District

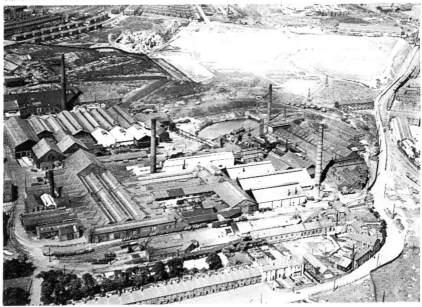

Cowley Hill Plate Glass Works

Acknowledgement St. Helens Local History and Archives Library.

148

18

ATTEMPTED TAKE OVER BID

The Float process was more than just a glassmaking process, especially to the industrialist, stockbroker, shareholder, etc, to them it was a money making machine because of its added assets in Licencing, income, royalties, etc., so prominent that in 1986/87 there was a take-over bid for Pilkington plc by B.T.R.

Here again the people grouped together as one big family to show their loyalty, trust, dependency and respect for the Pilkington glass industry, which is the world's largest Float glass industry.

This was a very critical time for Pilkington plc because it came at a time when the take-over bid could have easily been forgotten by many people, because it was during the Christmas and New Year festivity period, but no, not by the people of St Helens.

Everyone in Pilkingtons, and St Helens suddenly came to life, to declare war on B.T.R.

The people from all walks of life in St Helens, Politicians, Chamber of Commerce, Trades, Industries and even all the churches of every denomination, sent in recorded protests via Television, Radio, Press, letters to the Ministry of Trade, the Prime Minister, stickers on vehicles etc., and everything that was humanly possible was done to discourage the would be potential B.T.R. shareholder from bidding for the Pilkington Empire.

There was a protest march from the Pilkington Head Office in St Helens, to the St Helens Town Hall, headed by Members of Parliament, Clergymen, Politicians etc., and over 3,000 people taking part.

In addition a petition of over 25,000 signatures from the Chamber of Commerce and another one of over 5,000 signatures from the Churches of St Helens, were sent to the Minister of Trade and the Prime Minister.

All this gave encouragement to the Chairman of Pilkington plc, Mr Antony Pilkington (now Sir Antony), and his working team, who were working very hard behind the scenes, with shares, new shareholders and finance, etc., of which they proved themselves in doing a very good job of work.

Eventually B.T.R. gave up the struggle, for the fight of the Pilkington plc, to the delight of everyone.

Another example of St Helens and Pilkington team work!

19

CATS

Cats were a great asset to the glassworkers in many ways, and have been for longer than I can remember.

Where there are warm buildings like furnaces and all the designs like underground flues, steam, water, gas and oil pipes, drains etc. here we have a marvellous breeding ground for all types of vermin, such as rats, mice, crickets etc.

Although many types of poisons were put down to kill the vermin, it was not always possible to kill everything because of the vast number of breeding places. In winter time the warmth of the furnaces would encourage vermin from outside to come in, just like many millions of people are going abroad for the sunshine holidays.

The cat being the stalker, and hunter, of the rats, mice and crickets, did keep the vermin away from the glassmakers areas of work, like locker rooms, mess rooms, operators platforms etc. I am sure those days cats were part of the team.

One example, a float bath operator would be sat on his own, hour after hour, keeping the glass flow in control, which was a most warm, tiring and a monotonous job, especially on night shift, and believe me, it is so easy to doze off under those conditions during the night, but he had help from the cat, which would come and sit with him and more or less talk to him as animal lovers know. Yes practically every operator I knew of for many years had his own pet cat which would come along everytime the operator was on.

When the cat wasn't around especially during the night a mouse or rat has been known to run along the pipes and come out into the open looking for food and I have known times when on night shift the waste paper baskets had always a mouse or two in them.

The cats, especially the kittens, would catch and eat crickets but crickets made them thin, so some of the men brought milk and food to help the kittens to survive.

Some say a cat has nine lives but I am sure it must be more, because in a glass factory it is common to see them walking on glass, sleeping in the most dangerous places where it is dangerously hot for them, sometimes where glass is being broken, the cat could easily be cut, or blinded with glass splinters, for cats do not wear safety glasses, like people in dangerous areas, or protective clothing for hot work.

Amazingly I cannot remember seeing or hearing of a cat being badly bruised, cut or burned in our glass factory, unless it had been in a fight with a rat, or some other cat.

Today new and modern factories do not have the same vermin problems as the old factories did years ago so the cat is just a luxury pet, instead of a necessity pet, and as one man said, "My cat clocks in and out with me, don't you pal?" And the cat looked up at him, and grinned.

20

SAFETY & GASES

Gases have always been very important to the Glassmakers.

First we had the coal gas or better known to glassmakers as the Producer Gas, Second Gas Oil, and then North Sea Gas.

These are the gases we used on float glass furnaces.

On the Float Bath, there was first, burn't town's gas (or treated town's gas). Next, there was Nitrogen and Hydrogen.

The Health and Safety aspect of all these gases has been very important to all personnel and glassmaking qualities, but besides looking at the dangerous and serious aspects, I would like to mention some of the characters who contributed so well to the efficiency in the use of these gases.

The making of producer Gas was a real dirty hot dangerous, unhealthy job. When the coal was being fed into the producer, each time the operator opened the producer door, to drop the coal into the producer, a force of coal gas would flush out and the operator many a time would get a good sniff of dirty gas in his face and lungs.

Because of the type of work and the design of the coal gas producer, it was an everyday occurrence for a workman to complain of a headache or dizziness from gas leaks.

There was the oxygen, respirators, and the rocking stretchers that were used to revive any bad gassing cases and after treatment the victim would be seen by the works doctor.

It is well a known phrase for someone to say "ask a silly question and you get a silly answer".

One day a couple of Americans were looking round the gas producers, both tall men, smart and well educated, holding senior positions in their own firm back in America.

One of the workmen who was a small built man was approached by one of the Americans and the American said "Excuse me my good man. What do you make here?." The workman who was covered in coal-dust and sweating, looked up into the big American's face and said "Skeletons you daft b . . . . . ." The American smiled and walked away and that little episode fully summed up both situations.

On the furnaces or lehrs where the gas was in use, if a gas leak was suspected the methods of detection was by canaries.

At the works lodge a big cage was kept, which always had plenty of canaries inside it, and the man who was responsible for them got the nick name of "yellow bird", because of the colour of the birds.

Those days gas smells were a common smell around furnacies and lehrs and more or less accepted in the environment, but if the smell of gas became too strong, the workmen in the area would ask the foreman to bring yellow bird and his canaries.

The test was, if the canary died from the amount of gas in the area, then something had to be done urgently to repair the gas leak, but if the canary survived, then it was safe to work in the area.

First, when Nitrogen was used on the float bath, a gas the men had had no previous experience of, it became very frustrating for some of the men, but of course frustration can be used at will, either as an asset, or a debit in ignorance of the true chemistry of the gases.

Confidence with nitrogen was built up by the results of the canary test, because when a man complained of the nitrogen, someone would say we want yellow bird to test the gas leak, but the nitrogen did not affect the canaries as the other gases did, the canaries lived; also it was a big joke at the time that when we started using nitrogen there were more babies being produced by the wives which was a funny coincidence at the time.

Hydrogen was the most dangerous and highly explosive gas the men had to learn about as well as the other gases.

As glassmakers we needed some safe, practical, simple calculations which could be applied easily in cases of emergency.

We had in our Production department a man who had served as a pilot in the Polish Air Force. He had a PhD in chemistry, and whenever there was a doubt in our minds about fuels or gases, it was a compliment to him if we would listen while he explained to us in the easiest way he could.

This was an example. He said to me, "Look Tom, here is a method I know you will understand easily. The Bath Temperature for working conditions range from 1000°c to 600°C unless the bath is being cooled for a cold repair.

"There are no problems with nitrogen it is just a cooling, reducing pressurised gas.

"Hydrogen is highly explosive, but if you use the table of one percentage to every 100° centigrade in temperature it will be safe, with a nitrogen mixture.

"If the bath temperature is 1000°C then 90% nitrogen and 10% hydrogen is safe, but never go higher than the 10% hydrogen, work on that scale but remember, once the bath comes down to a temperature of 300°C then shut off the hydrogen completely and just have the 100% nitrogen to create a pressurised reducing atmosphere in the bath.

"But also there is fitted a fail safe valve in the system which means that if there is any fault in the nitrogen supply, then the hydrogen valve will automatically close and prevent a hydrogen build up to the bath so then there would be no danger of an explosion."

The next gas was SO_2. This was used at the front entrance to the lehr under the glass ribbon.

By this time we had the more up to date methods of gas detections like instruments and soap tests, but unsupervised and uncontrolled, the dangers to man, plant and glassmaking were always there.

Pilkington Research Laboratories Lathom

156

21

SECURITY

The security system that was essential to the success of Float Glass was very well planned, carried out and respected by all employees.

There were many reasons why the security programme was given an industrial priority.

(a) When the float experiment was moved from a small pilot plant to a large production plant, many more employees were needed, more rules and regulations to be implemented on a much larger scale, which resulted in the float bath area being sealed off completely from the furnace and the lehr.

(b) In the float bath area in the beginning there was something we could almost describe as an experimental time bomb, made up of the following ingredients which could have been pilfered or damaged easily.

(c) There was in excess of £500,000 liquid tin in the bath, with a reserve quota on site.

(d) We had several uses of platinum which amounted to several thousands of pounds.

(e) New type of technical services, tools and accessories in abundance.

(f) Most important — the float glass experiment itself.

With the float bath area being screened off by metal sheets, and a security man permanently at the doorway, no unauthorised person could see what was going on around the float bath section and at that time it was said: "It is easier to get in and out of Fort Knox than the float bath area".

We had a system which personnel who were permanently stationed and working on the float bath had a small yellow badge with their own number on it, no one else could use the badge and the men were personally responsible for their own badges and wearing them whilst at work.

Anyone else, from director to workman, who visited the float bath, no matter what it was for, had to sign a book and wear a special numbered badge which was a red one, and then after the visit to sign out and return the red badge.

The security men were very strict with everyone and I have known times when a director or senior manager has walked into the float bath area absentmindedly without signing, but they were always brought back to sign and acknowledge security.

As time went on it was noticeable that all personnel were very proud and assisted in all ways to help security.

We had a foreman who had every quality required for his job, really experienced, honest and proud, and security conscious.

There was also a shop steward of the float bath department who was a very good, reliable, experienced and hard worker, and he was very proud of his job and the achievement of the work the men were doing.

One Saturday afternoon, the shop steward decided to show one of his union pals the float process — this was unofficial.

To do this they had to by-pass the gate man which was successful, but while they were both in the float bath section they were spotted by the foreman who was security conscious.

The foreman reported the incident to the works police patrol man, who escorted the shop steward and his union pal out of the building and reported the incident to the works manager. The shop steward was suspended and then sacked.

Owing to the shop stewards excellent workmanship both at work and in union matters, the area leaders of the G.M.W.U. appealed to Lord Harry Pilkington for his reinstatement which after many meetings was granted, this proved to be a decision that was approved by all, because the same shop steward had a loyalty to Pilkington's, union, workmen, and his family, that was admired by everyone, for he never shirked any problem, or pulled any punches in his speech to defend, or attack firm or union as was necessary at the time.

As we are all aware, pilfering has always happened and probably always will, especially in factories, offices, shops etc, maybe in a small way, say a pencil, rubber, nut or bolt etc, or maybe someone higher pilfering the accounts. Few get caught out. Many don't, because the security system is not good enough, or the amount of pilfering and the cost of better security would be too expensive to operate.

There was a new difference, something our workforce and security had never experienced in the glass industry for we had a float bath with over ½ million pounds worth of molten tin inside it. Access to the tin could be gained along each side of the float bath at several points, sometimes when there were problems, the hot tin would leak out of the exit end of the float bath and there would be tin in cold pieces lying around and those days there was no television cameras or warning systems to indicate anyone was taking tin out of the float bath which resulted in a high degree of trust expectancy from the workforce because of the easy access to higher values.

All this happened at a time in the early period of licensing and those days security was stretched to the limit around the bath area, because, more and more, licensees were working around the float bath area.

The licensees had only licensed the float bath but as glass makers they were very interested in the furnaces etc. and other sections of the factory, for this purpose, special routes to and from the float bath were used for the licensees, and when they were training in the float bath area, many a little excuse would be tried out by them to look over the screens to look at the furnace, but the security people and workers kept a very close watch so this could not happen.

There was a period when there was a team over from Germany being trained.

At that time the German team had a locker room near the float bath area, and with the Pilkington workers and the licensee workers mixing together both in work and socially, it was natural for both lots of workers to trust each other to the extent that the German team did not lock the door to their locker room, they only locked their respective lockers, to which each one had a personal key.

It was about halfway through the training period that one of the German team reported his locker had been broken open and his money had been stolen, this happened again to another member of the German team a few days later; of course, everyone, the full German team and our workmen felt they were under suspicion, which was a worrying time for some of them. Our security people were baffled to the extent that the finger print experts were called in.

The police caught the culprit, and we were all amazed to find it was one of the German team, who had been stealing from the lockers.

When the German team leader was questioned about this man he confessed he knew very little about his personal background and he told us that the man had only been taken on two months previously, before coming to St Helens for training.

The man was sacked immediately and sent back to Germany. This was a relief to our glassmakers.

I have given a few examples of the different types of security practices our glassmakers had to be aware of, not only in St. Helens but in many countries abroad, because they were mixing, training and working with so many unknown people they had to be always security conscious, industrial, and personnel at all times.

Many a time a licensee would try to bring a camera into the factory, but cameras were banned at all times and because of the good security system we had, none succeeded.

As one man used to say, working in the float bath area those days "Big Brother's eyes were always on them from all industrial angles".

There was one of the shifts and instead of the men calling each other by their Christian names, many a time they would call them by their badge number, just like a convict or calling a boat on a lake with a number on it.

Yes there was plenty of humour and joking about the badges as well as the seriousness of the security, which had to be, because of the hard work, team happiness and efficiency, otherwise the men would have been bored; with all the restrictions being imposed on them which was unknown to other departments and jobs.

22

ST. HELENS

Before the float line known as Greengate was built the site was a real eyesore for the St. Helens people.

The reason being was that many years ago Pilkington had their own brick works and their own coal mining works in this area.

When the coal mining and brick making ceased what was left was a huge pit or hole in the ground, plus coal slag heaps.

Over a period of years the St. Helens Council and Pilkingtons filled in the huge hole with rubbish.

Eventually everywhere was settled down and levelled off creating a wide open space.

Pilkingtons decided to build a new float line on the spacious land, it is a massive factory producing 6,000 tons per week.

This float line can be seen for many miles around set in a country garden environment with its gardens, trees, lawns, etc, with transport access to the main motorways.

It is set in an area next to a beautiful garden area known as Sherdley Park, and with this area being higher than the St Helens town centre area, people in St Helens can pin-point and see at a glance the new environments of tomorrow's factories.

While standing in St. Helens looking at Greengate if we look over to the right there is the huge 12 storey building of the Pilkington Head Office which is a beautiful building set in garden and pool surrounds of its own, at another high point on

161

the St Helens boundary. The planning of this came in the early days when expansion was anticipated along with the float glass invention for world wide administration purposes.

Next we came nearer to the town centre, the sheet glass factory. This factory had many furnaces with tall chimneys pouring out smoke, also the warehousing and sheet tanks were conspicuously high with as many as 6—8 floors, again all factory buildings were in a compact area and at certain times of the year this created a dirty murky atmosphere around the town centre, giving St. Helens a dull environment.

With the progress of float glass invention all the sheet glass furnaces and buildings have now been demolished, which left a lot of open spaces near the town centre, which is now being redeveloped chiefly for municipal purposes of which St. Helens hope to benefit by in the near future, with trade and jobs, e.g. superstores, hotels, etc.

In terms of factory buildings, the float process has contributed to a better and healther industry giving the town a much improved look to encourage other industrialists to come to St. Helens.

Pilkington have also set a lead in this area which has given the St. Helens Council every type of encouragement to reorganise their own works, buildings, sites, estates and derelict open spaces, of which they have done a marvellous job.

Because when you can see all the surrounds of a town being changed for the better then it is obvious the centre is ultimately going to follow and I believe this was the beginning of not only a revolution in glass making but a contribution also to a modern structural and design of town changes.

Let us now have a look at how the changes in the Pilkington industry affected the people of St. Helens.

If we turn the clock back 15-20 years or maybe 10 years there were plenty of jobs in St. Helens, for St. Helens was a boom town compared to many other towns, because there were so many industries in and around St. Helens.

Many of the industries around the area were work related to Pilkington, e.g. the coal, engineering, brick and building industries, were all partly reliant on the glass industry for many of their jobs and orders, which also helped the trade and commerce departments of St. Helens to flourish, this also helped the local council to spread its wings in improvements, and spending which they took advantage of.

162

As new technology came along at Pilkingtons people were being asked to take voluntary redundancy. This was a signal for several other industries in the area to do the same, the emphasis being put on high wages, high throughput, trade competition, and low profits.

This resulted in many thousands of people being put out of work and the ones hit the hardest were the school leavers, aged 16 and upwards especially the 16-18 year-old who had no 'O' levels and even then there were no jobs for the better qualified because the whole glass industry was not recruiting but reducing the work forces which was a disaster for the workers, especailly for their children and grandchildren.

The real shock came in the mid 1970's when the Western world was hit by the first oil shock and the Japanese electronic industry started to overrun its western competition, this killed about 2,000 jobs in St. Helens.

This was the beginning of job losses of which the labour numbers employed by Pilkington began to roll down the steep hill gathering losses each year, mainly due to new technology.

St. Helens being the strong minded town it is, did not just lie down and let this disaster happen without doing something about it, they fought back against such depredations of change and recession and formed what was known as the Community of St. Helens Trust to decrease the risks involved of St. Helens having all its employment eggs in too few baskets.

This Trust venture was the brainchild of Pilkingtons and proved to be a great success in the creation of many new jobs in the town.

The St.Helens Council were also very concerned about the unemployment situation that was developing in the town and they co-operated with the Trust, and assisted the finance of St. Helens Trust in 1978/79/80 from the urban programme funds by £60,000.

St. Helens Council began many schemes to create employment to assist in removing the despondancy through job losses.

They created new industrial estates, created jobs, surveying roads, sewers, all back up services like electricity, gas, water etc.

Money was spent on advertising and publicity at £50,000 per year.

In the ten year period between 1978 to 1988 there were 733 new companies formed in the St. Helens area.

They did everything possible to co-operate with anyone who

would bring jobs to St. Helens no matter what type of work or industry it was.

If we look at the numbers of total council employees (all grades) manual, and clerical in 1975 the numbers were 6,435. Now in 1988 the numbers are 9,414.

This council and the Trust are still working hard on creating new jobs for St. Helens and succeeding, which is slowly but surely reducing the unemployment numbers each year, in plain language they have got on their bikes doing their best for St Helens which has given the people a better frame of mind to accept new technology and its effects much more easily than if no one had done anything only moan.

The council must be congratulated on the way recruitment is progressing and most important is that school leavers who have not got enough 'O' or 'A' levels for industry are finding jobs with the council. These youngsters are being given permanent jobs and being schooled at the same time, also in Y.T.S. jobs as well.

Sheet Works before Float.   Acknowledgement St. Helens Local History and Archives Library.

23

SUMMARY

We needed a new process because of the market demand and economies of glassmaking. With plate glass it was very costly, labour intensive, because 20% was ground off and slurried as waste, with land space diminishing.

The company gave priority to the discovery of a means of reducing or even eliminating altogether the grinding and polishing process, so more scientists and engineers were recruited for this purpose.

Pilkington being the ambitious company they were, had always many experiments going to improve glass quality, and had gained a little experience as to the reaction of tin to glass, e.g. tin was used to weight refractroy tubes to check glass flows in furnaces, tin had been tried as a conveyor of glass at various temperatures around 600°C so what we had was tin used at 1600°C and tin used at 600°C the middle temperature experiment was missing, but only temporarily.

One of the brilliant engineers who had been recruited was Alastair Pilkington who was not related to the St. Helens Pilkington family in any way, and began work at Pilkington in August 1947, and became involved in experimental work at Cowley Hill Works between 1949 and 1951.

In 1951 he was posted as Production Manager at the Plate Glass factory in Doncaster.

It was in 1952 at a manufacturing conference he suggested the possibility of fire-finishing glass by floating it on a bath of molten tin in a neutral atmosphere at around 1,000°C and float it frictionless down a bath, through a temperature gradient falling to about 600°C at which temperature the ribbon of glass would be cool enough to be taken off on steel rollers, without marking the glass surfaces so that grinding and polishing would not be necessary. Also, knowing that the specific gravity of tin was much greater than that of glass, it would be an amicable supporter of the glass, and was likely to acquire strictly parallel surfaces as it floated down the bath, thus eliminating the grinding and polishing process. This was his job, and he did it well. A good idea, but where is the money coming from?

The British economy was enjoying a post war boom, and the company's profits had risen sharply and the expected glass demand for future years had reached massive proportions.

Hard work on the pilot plants which had been put down for experimental purposes had shown promising results, but not definite results to encourage the Board to decide to take the plunge and risk the amount of approximately £200,000 for the building of a float line for further development and production purposes, or put down another long inefficient grinding and polishing line at a huge cost.

The Board took the plunge and built the float line (what a brave decision to take). Here is a perfect example of the guts of the Pilkington family Board as it was mostly family guided in those days.

Having seen the light as to the money problems, the next problem was how do we achieve success? For at this time not one piece of saleable glass had been achieved.

Many people from director to workman had their doubts about the ultimate result.

Unknown to the pessimists, a silent hard working team of optimists was working, and training very hard, comprising of development and production glass workers, giving their very best attention to the unknown results hoping for success.

Success on the float line was looking very dim, and the cost of developing the process was far greater than had been anticipated, and much more money was needed, and the cost at this point ran out at about £900,000 per year.

It was about 14 months after much of trial and error work on the production float line by the team, that the first piece of saleable glass was made, then we could all see the glimmer of

166

light at the end of the tunnel.

Eventually in 1959 the process was announced to the public.

In the year 1962/63 the first foreign licence was sold, and the process began to show an uninterrupted profit from then to the present day.

From the first licensees in 1962/63 many more of our competitors came along for licenses to the effect that Pilkington have always had since 1962/1963 a profitable float licensing income each year of millions of pounds, and even as at this current year, income licensing (mainly from float) and technical fees is running at the rate of £30 million per year and is liable to continue for many years to come, as each year new licenses are being granted. What a beautiful inherited bonanza the shareholders have picked up, some of them without doing any work at all for it, only moaning as the share prices fluctuate.

How was all this actually achieved. I am sure I have explained this in the reading of this book, but as I have quoted so many times the whole world benefited by the sacrifices of the few glassmakers' families.

It was most ironical that during this period of time Lord Pilkington was the most outstanding Chairman the family had provided, he had complete faith in the float process during all its difficulties in the early development stages, and its success owes so much to him for his experienced, guided knowledge and guts to produce success from failures.

There is little doubt that if the company had been public at that time in the 1950's the shareholders would not have taken the financial risk, which would have ultimately taken the glass industry away from St. Helens.

The development work was just like a huge jigsaw puzzle, as fast as one little piece was slipped into the middle space, another one at the side or corner proved it was not the matching piece to complete the picture. It was trial and error for many years, with all interested parties having a bash, creating headache after headache, some could go away for a rest and an aspirin and some could not, they had to stand guard and make sure no one disturbed pieces that fitted, and in some instances found pieces that fitted and actually fitted them.

As the whole world was progressing into a new glass age, the age of float glass, and licensees were buying licenses, each foreign licensee was thinking new, taking a leaf out of the Pilkington book.

They were planning for the future on new green field sites, or even on desert land making sure that the new float lines had also plenty of back up factory space, and leaving room for further expansion in the coming years.

Each new factory could easily be recognised by the design, as they were all similar in length, height and width, with their tall chimneys, water cooling towers, long conveyors for conveying the cullet and materials from mixing room, warehousing buildings etc. It looked as though they had all been pre-fabricated and shipped out in boxes from England; practically everyone alike, North, South, East and West of the globe.

Coming back to the float glass line worker once more. All these buildings and designs were no problem to build as far as the licensees were concerned, because world wide there are engineers, electricians, builders, architects and every type of profession required, all understanding each others' professions and trades.

The only job they did not know, was how to make float glass and this is where our float glass foremen and men were really needed and excelled.

This process did not only change glassmaking methods, but made huge changes in the back-up industries like building, engineering, changed landmarks, and new towns being built gave new environmental aspects.

In many countries it was noticeable even when visiting for the first time just before start-up, I could pin-point the float glass factory in the distance before I got to it.

There it was its huge chimney, high water tower, huge long buildings, all new, sticking out just like the beginning of a new city in the desert, (glass originated from the desert). No-one, nowhere, worldwide escaping this miracle.

All this may sound fantastic and unreal but seeing is believing.

Yes, the workmen and foremen on the float glass lines still going strong faithful and loyal to job, and Pilkington, travelling here, there and everywhere, training and working with every type of licensee worldwide and in many different types of environment. Let us remember the workmen worldwide are in classes of their own, and wherever our workmen went they had to abide with the most convenient accommodation as near to the factory as possible, and in many instances these were far below British working class standards but they soldiered on.

The training by the trades, technical research and development people and professional people was started and extended in the schools, classrooms, universities etc. before going to the Barrack Rooms. The glassmakers did all their training under fire, right from the start to finish, with only glassmakers to train glassmakers.

At a party one night, a lady in no uncertain terms, put it over very well and created a laugh for everyone because she was upset about her husband going away. She said the foreigners did not need the tradesmen, technicians, professional people, they had plenty of those people of their own, who could read and copy. What they wanted were the sweat tubs to teach them how to make float glass (meaning glassmakers).

Travelling around the world reminded me of my war travels when people used to say "he is on a Cook's Tour" and this happened to many people, but it included for these people many different battle fronts with hard times.

This was a similar position for the glassmakers, but there was no war, and always they had to be on their best behaviour under many trying circumstances with the end product of good glassmaking.

Differences before float and after as regards to flat glass production in the U.K. From 1948-1988 if we graph the production in tonnage per week the mean line would be near enough on today's figures of 14,000 tons per week, except for a recessional period in 1975-1980, and as we are in a new glass world and have been for the past eight years or so, no improvement is outstanding in U.K. figures.

Personnel in 1948 working in the flat glass factories in the UK producing approximately 14,000 tons of glass per week was 11,454 people.

Personnel in 1988 working at the two flat glass factories producing approximately, 14,000 tons of glass per week is Cowley Hill 862 people and at Greengate UK5 is 391 people which is a total of 1,253, a reduction of 10,201 people in the flat glass factories.

The figures do not include Watson Street for production as rolled and wired glasses are still being made.

It is quite easy for me to say what have our sales experts been doing? But without the home production float lines in the UK only our overseas competitors are going to gain in a glass world.

We must always remember that no matter where we invest in

foreign countries, whether it be a Pilkington factory or not, that these people may make us many profits, or help us to get plenty of customers and trade, as far as the British economy and jobs go they are still our competitors, and as the big wheel turns every so often we get the recessions, the people we have lost trade to by under producing in England, we will not get it back in a hurry if at all. Pilkington built up their wealth and strength through people and this is what profits are all about, the employment of people. We could never hope to carry out a revolution of industry again without the working classes, and these people have now been discarded for profits (some false profits).

From experience I know the production workers are also one of the firm's biggest assets in customer relations and assistance in glass complaints. When the customers visit the factories many a little problem is eased and understood, and sometimes ironed out by the Public Relations people, sometimes resulting in a better understanding of the problems both customer and Pilkington encounter during the visit, resulting in more sales. Some of the finest sales people are practical workers talking to customers for it is surprising the number of people in all walks of life who said I have read about the Float Process but I had absolutely no idea of how fascinating it was untill I saw it for myself on site, and have had it explained by the practical men.

Looking at the Flat Glass industry world wide, the Float Glass invention has really been something of a world summit agreement, all producing countries coming to an industrial understanding which is common to every one of them, this is like a miracle, in good international working and personnel relationships.

The other miracle was the economics of it all, because even before the Float Glass invention had mastered the art of good glass making, glass manufacturers were coming from all parts of the world, buying licences to make Float Glass, and there was not a need to spend money on advertising the process like we have to do today with the glass products. The workmanship of the Float Line glassworkers was a great contributing advert.

As we are all aware of the stresses which were put on the Float Line glassworkers and their families, it is only natural that because we are all made different some were beginning to feel the strain of the strenuous hard responsible work at an early age than they would have done with a normal job of work, because

170

the type of hard work worked for many years was well beyond the normal type of hot glass making work, actually it was abnormal, it was a miracle how many years they had to persevere with it.

Unfortunatelly for some of the families, sickness and ill-health began to show at an early age and it is to the families and children of these men the success of the Float Process owes so much.

While writing this book I have been more or less looking through the glass window from the outside, into the inside, of the float glass invention, making comments on the success, and failures and contribution made by Pilkington teams and families which is marvellous and is a great honour for these people to be a part of it, which I know they are really proud about it all.

Let us now look from the inside of the glass window to the outside and see what a wonderful creation we have been involved in which is something money could never buy.

Glass was God's creation to be advanced by man.

Thousands of years ago the sun, and the desert sands, and fire, was the first signal to glass.

As years went by, man improved on the glass quality.

Today, glass is a shining light in the whole world which is a massive contribution in the turning of darkness into light, so let us have a look at this contribution.

Looking through the glass we can see all the beautiful things in this world, on land, sea or air, no matter where it is, things like flowers, birds, fish, beautiful scenery etc.

If we are many miles away by using glass telescopes or binoculars we can see the light of the world in far away places.

In the growing of food, glass has been a great assett as to the extra food needed for the growth in population.

Glass gives us light in our sight and minds, where without it, we would be in the darkness when protecting ourselves from outside forces.

We also use it in the form of spectacles, to enable us to see the light of the world better.

I will finish with the greatest assett, the mirror. We look into the mirror, then go away and forget what we look like, we need more glass and more mirrors and we need to look in them more often so we won't forget who we are and what we look like.

This book has brought back many memories of the job, countries, and people and I can thank God, for giving me the privilege of knowing and working with all who contributed in anyway no matter how small or large it was and especially all families concerned in making the Float Process a worldwide success.

Something the people of St Helens are really proud of and can say "We Made It".

A tribute to St Helens
and its glassmakers

by Tom Grundy

Printed by Chalon Press Limited
Units 1-4 Chalon Way Industrial Estate
Chalon Way St Helens England WA10 1AU
Telephone St Helens (0744) 69 6395/6 Fax (0744) 451617